The Thunderbird Review

2021

Issue No. 9

The Thunderbird Review
2021
Issue No. 9

Editorial Staff
Joy Armstrong
Jessica Penn
Joseph Bruce

Faculty Advisor
Darci Schummer

All correspondence should be addressed to the anthology@fdltcc.edu.

Cover art "Ancestor's Treasure Chest and Reindeer Antlers" by Marlene Wisuri

Cover design by Darci Schummer, Joy Armstrong, and Joseph Bruce

ISBN-13: 9798582632368

A Note from the Editorial Staff:

We hope you enjoy the 2021 issue of *The Thunderbird Review,* an art and literary anthology produced by Fond du Lac Tribal and Tribal and Community College.

The past year was challenging for many—our daily lives and routines were interrupted, the way we connect with others was transformed, and the shadows of illness and death haunted us. As always, the release of our journal marks the spring. Hopefully, the release of this particular issue will also mark something greater than that: the beginning of a return to normality, even if that normal isn't exactly the same as before.

We received many submissions from students and professional writers alike, from new contributors and those we have proudly published in the past. Some highlights of this journal are the opening essay, beautifully co-written by Govinda Budrow and Babette Sandman, that takes us through the experience of homelessness; the closing essay by Carter Meland that contemplates the author's relationship with Bagwajinini; and Tricia Gottschalk's powerful essay about growing up in foster care. Bradley Limanen's short story "How to Cure Sorrow (And Why You Shouldn't)" uses fantasy to get at the human experience, and we have also been blessed with wonderful poetry by Jill Lindl, Jan Chronister, Deborah Rasmussen and others. We hope you enjoy reading these pieces as much as we did.

If you would like to help with the next issue of the *Thunderbird Review,* please let us know. We welcome students as well as members of the community. Questions or comments can be directed to anthology@fdltcc.edu.

Sincerely,

The Editorial Staff of the *Thunderbird Review*

Table of Contents

Poetry

Creative Nonfiction/Memoir

Fiction

Artwork

Contributors' Notes

Homeless: A Lullaby from a Mother to a Daughter
Babette Sandman and Govinda Budrow

It is said that a lullaby is a "universal language sung by a mother to her child" and a lullaby is "used to pass down cultural knowledge or tradition." This is the lullaby I spoke to my child when she was ready to turn four years old.

I did not expect it to happen. Nobody does but it did. One moment, I was hopeful and saw it all ahead of me how this was going to happen and in one meeting it all changed. I was young, a single mother, and I thought I found someone, maybe I found love, and travelled with him to Boulder, Colorado. It was a great trip from Watersmeet, Michigan, on a reggae bus to Boulder. Listening to reggae music the whole way and hanging out with Rastafarians and others on the bus was a beautiful journey! Arriving in Boulder was a shock. The person I thought we were going to be with was homeless! This spiritual man I thought I met suddenly turned into a very different person when we got off that bus. I immediately went to the county welfare office as I was raised on welfare and I knew they could help me get set up here until I found a job to take care of us. It was our turn next to talk to the lady at her desk. I told her I was new in the area and I just need help to get a place for us to live as I planned to get a job. She looked at me coldly and said, "This is the richest county in Colorado and what are YOU doing here?" WOW! I could not believe it. Then she said, "You will need your own room, mailbox, and cupboard for your food, and we will check! Until then, we can't help you." That day, I walked out of the welfare office holding my little girl's hand, homeless. Nobody knew me, I was not from here. We began to walk our first steps as homeless people and that was when it hit me. This whole different person inside of me emerged. We were going to survive this! I was not scared, sad, or worried or any of these feelings one would think you would have in this moment. A part of me knew I had no time for that and all I could be right now is focused, aware, and on the hunt for food in a concrete jungle. I became aware that my little girl did not know the situation she was in. She had my hand and trusted me. That was the first time I looked into her eyes with my newfound strength knowing I would need to keep her comforted through this. I spoke my first lullaby to her, "Home is right here," as I held my hand to my heart and in the area where she had breast fed for over two years.

This is home. She looked at me with her dark eyes and the same strength that I had found in myself I could see she felt it too.

Your first memories as a child are locked in through their novelty. Something out of the ordinary will stand out to you. I always thought my first memory was a moment of standing on the edge of a large body of water. My mind created it as the ocean, but trees surrounded this water. My mind put these pieces together and out of sequence as a little girl. I remember this moment washing dishes in a lake. Scrubbing with the sand in a large kettle. This was routine except for this day. This day a fish jumped into the kettle and I lifted it up with so much glee. I had plans and a bond already forming to this little fish. I turned my head to share this excitement and the fish jumped out. Back to the water. Memory ends. Where was I? Why was I there? I know my mother was there. She was always there. She was home for me.

I met people right away that were helpful or did the Creator put people in our path that would help? A woman I met offered her backyard so we would have a place to sleep. It was chilly that first night and I had no blankets for us. I knew what I had to do. I made sure they were rich people because I learned from my dad to never steal from the poor. I lost my dad to a prison system when I was young and always connected with him when he got out of prison or jail. I missed him and when he was around to be a dad, he was a good dad. I found him in the alleys of downtown Duluth where he drank. He taught me a lot of things as I believe he wanted me to be like him. His lifestyle did not appeal to me and by age 16, I knew I would never be like him. At that moment, however, as I prepared myself to steal a blanket, I could hear his teaching to make sure they are rich. The house was all lit up with the curtains open. I could see everything inside. I do not know where the people were at that moment, but my eyes zoomed in on a blanket hanging over the banister on the stairs. I crept in and grabbed it and ran out of the house to my daughter who was anxiously waiting. We went to the backyard offered by a stranger to us, complete strangers. We cuddled in that blanket and I spoke my lullaby to her whispering, "Home is right here as I touched my heart, wherever I am is where home is."

That night, I stood alone watching the window with all the bright lights. I was nervous. This was different and that is why I remember it. Sleeping in new places or outside was not in my memories. Watching my mother that night sneak into this house to gather a blanket to keep us warm is a memory. I didn't feel alone though. Somehow, it felt like others were waiting with me. They comforted me in the moments that passed. Decades later, retelling this story and my mother told me that we were all alone. No one waited with me for her to return with that blanket. I can still feel them in that memory, although I never saw them or heard them.

Things fell in place in the homeless world. For instance, homeless people are so kind and know where the food is being served or given out. They knew of my daughter and I and always let us know where to eat or shared food with us although they were homeless too. They never hung around us concealing our homelessness situation. Women like me were losing their children if social services found out. I instantly became a top executive director! In the morning, I could always find a discarded newspaper that I snapped open and sat proud having a cup of coffee looking serious at the paper. No homeless people here! Sometimes I told people what I needed by stating with great confidence, "Give me a dollar," which they did as they hardly knew what to do with that. I got my coffee and a clove cigarette. I knew where to go for food and the homeless people watched over us keeping us in mind, handing us apples or muffins. I kept my daughter fed and did not eat until she was done eating. One store employee in the back of the grocery store caught me taking fruit out of the crate that he just threw out calling it bruised fruit. He said, "If you can be here at 10:00 every day, I will set a crate of fruit on top of the garbage dumpster because by law I have to." Every day, we went there and got our fresh fruit. Was he a good person who wanted to help or did the Creator work through him to help us? We learned to live homeless. I pounded the streets dragging my little girl with me looking for a job. The man I thought was spiritual became an abuser, so I had to survive that too. How did this spiritual man respected by all, blessing children become so abusive? I went down to 109 pounds. I continued to look into my daughter's dark eyes and always speak the lullaby to comfort her, "Home is right here as I touched my heart. Home is where mama is," as I held her tightly to my chest. Before she was born, I had a dream about a little girl about 3 years old who looked into my eyes with her dark eyes. She was surrounded by white clouds and as she looked beyond my eyes into my soul she said, "You are my spiritual guide, and I am going to watch everything you do." After she was born, I recognized her right away, the little girl from my dream with those dark eyes. This dream comforted me as no matter what situation I was in, she was watching me, and I was going to show her we could make it!

Lullabies do not hide the imperfections. Lullabies are the truth sung with such soothing grace that you are comforted in inflicted moments. My mother never hid the truth from me. She would gently rub my forehead back through my hair and tell me stories. Stories with great spiritual meanings and messages. These stories comforted me with the knowledge there were bigger things in this realm and faith was all I needed. Each step that she took, she allowed me to walk beside her. Many mothers would shield the eyes of their children or tell them lies to comfort their minds. I needed to walk with her and to see her. I demanded the truth. She showed me the truth and in turn, taught me about love, survival, stories and transformation.

Many people helped us, but it was not getting us off the streets. I could not find a job and did not have a phone number so they could call me. I feared my abusive boyfriend. People from Wallace Black Elk's vision quest site in the mountains above Boulder came to help us. Again, was it the people who came to help us or did the Creator send them? They said, "Come on, Babette, get your things. We are going to help." We got into the back of their truck with our little red suitcase and off we went way up into the mountains, turned up an access road, and finally the truck came to a stop. My daughter and I climbed out of the back of the truck with our suitcase, and we backed up a little as a huge man approached us. He said, "Ahow! I'm Wallace Black Elk. Can you cook?" "Yes," I said. "You can stay in that tipi over there. You will also have to go in the sweat every night to pray for the people on the hill," he said as he looked up. We were down in a bowl and all these people were on top of the hill on a vision quest. My daughter and I went into the tipi with our red suitcase. We had a place. I spoke the lullaby to her. "Home is where I am," as I touched my heart cuddling her to my chest." Once in awhile we would open the red suitcase and organize the small number of belongings we had. We would fold and organize our clothes nice and set the suitcase aside. Housework done!

Traveling children and children that grow up homeless have very little artifacts that survive their travels. I have few baby pictures. No toys or clothes to pass down to children. Only the things that you can carry can come with you. Our memories and our mother's stories serve as the videos and the snap shots of our lives. I remember this camp. There were many children. My mother years later would tell the story of how I organized the children in the camp within moments. She said, "You were always going to be a teacher" as she recalled these interactions. I had none of those beginnings that are often lifted in education. I had never watched television. I had stories told to me but no books. I had no home. I only had my mother and a small red suitcase.

I cooked and served coffee and every night I went into the sweat lodge to pray for the people on the hill. My daughter and I had a place to be and it felt good. I still would cuddle her and speak my lullaby to her, "Home is here as I touched my heart, where mama is, this is home." Wallace prayed for us every night to be able to go back to the Ojibwe people and find a home where the wind does not blow through. We stayed at the vision quest site above Boulder in the mountains through the summer and as vision quest camp started packing up to leave, we also left carrying Wallace Black Elk's prayers with us with hope for a better life.

This did not happen right away. We went to Denver with my boyfriend/abuser to stay with a relative of his. It is easy to trust someone who is violent when they are charming toward you making it feel like a fresh start. We ended up at his relative's house, a woman with three young children. This woman went out that night as we stayed and watched her children. They all went to sleep in the one bedroom they shared, and we slept in the front room. In the middle of the night, she came home drunk and started beating up her kids who went from sound asleep to screaming! It was awful to listen to and I was up the rest of the night. The woman finally passed out. My boyfriend started getting abusive again and I distinctly remember feeling that we were standing in the depths of darkness, a hell I could barely glimpse at. I grabbed my little girl's hand and went out into the residential street of Denver. It was very hot outside, and it was early in the morning. The sun was almost blinding as we emerged from such a darkness. We walked aimlessly to get blocks away from this place having no idea where we were going. Hot, tired, and thirsty with no money, we just kept walking. I could barely speak my lullaby to my daughter, but I had to. "Home is right here as I touched my heart, right here." We kept walking and we were surprised to hear a voice call out to us from the 3rd floor of an apartment building. "Hey," he said. "You look thirsty. Why don't you come up here and have something cold to drink?" That sounded so good on this hot day. When we went in, I was amazed at how beautiful the women were in the front room dressed like they just stepped out of a Vogue magazine. It was odd too because it was not noon yet and they were wearing evening wear for "going out on the town." They were outstandingly beautiful with hair and make-up professionally done. I was mesmerized by them as they looked at me and smiled. The man who invited us up gave us something cold to drink and noticed how tired we were. He gave us a room we very much appreciated and told us to rest. We would be alright and needed to rest. My little girl and I slept and relaxed there for two days. It felt so good! Nobody knew we were here. We could just rest! Occasionally, however, he would come in and I would tense up wondering what he wanted from me. He never made a move on me and he was very kind. He said they are going to take me to get a new wardrobe of clothes. I thought about the women in the front room. Wow! I could look like them! He mentioned this a few times in those two days. The second night he said tomorrow was my turn. They were taking me shopping. A small voice began to grow inside me, whispering to get out of there. A growing conflict emerged at the same time—a whole new wardrobe?! Wait a minute, they said nothing about my daughter. What about my daughter? None of those women in the front room had children that I could see. The voice grew louder: Get out! Get out! RUN! I grabbed my daughter and told her we had to run. We waited for a moment going past those women. We got to the door opened it and ran. He came out the door as those women must have told him we were running. He came to the door as we were running down the hallway. He yelled, "Get back here or I am going to put a contract out on you to have you killed!" We ran and did not look back. He did not know *much about me and I was homeless, which strangely comforted me because I knew he would not find me. I know now that I had met a sex trafficker who was spinning his web of lies around me preying on my vulnerability. To this day, I shudder to think of what their plan for my daughter was.*

My mother was a master at the lullaby. I rarely have moments that I was fearful in my childhood. Most often, she opened the world of goodness to my eyes. That day, I was afraid. I remember running on the concrete sidewalk. Afraid Clark would find us. Afraid these men would catch us. Running. We are exposed on these streets, but I see squarely in my memories that bus stop. I see it from across the street. It means something. It means safety.

We made it to the bus stop where it was a $3.00 ride between Denver and Boulder. We needed to get out of this place of darkness. We sat next to an older woman and told her everything that had just happened to us. She listened and told me I had done the right thing. It seemed we spent the rest of the day at that bus station. We listened to a man speak of losing his entire family to a fire. He was the only survivor. I looked around at the people sitting at the bus station waiting. We, along with others, had come to the crossroads where our next choices were crucial in setting a course for our life. Somehow, we eventually got on the bus back to Boulder.

Back in Boulder, it did not take long for me to have to get away from this increasingly violent situation. I ended up in the emergency room getting stitches in my head and the people who took me in that were ready to give a spot to sleep, and a cupboard for my food, an address, so I could get help from social services said I had to leave because of the violence. The emergency room doctor told me I could die from this. I had never heard this before. The advocates who worked in the Battered Women's Movement yelled at me, "You're a battered woman!" I had no idea what that was. I had nowhere to go and I had to be out by noon that day. I called 911 and asked for help. I had to meet a woman at the courthouse. My daughter and I hitch hiked there with our red suitcase. As we waited for her, I spoke my lullaby to my daughter, "Home is right here as I touched my heart, where I am is where home is." The lady took us to the shelter for battered women. I hated it at first as I felt that now, we were on skid row, the dog pound, and this was the worst. In no time after being there a day, I knew this was the best thing for us, a chance to get off the streets, be safe, rest and have a bed to sleep in! I hated my advocate at first. I saw her parking her car as I looked out the window. I knew she was coming to talk to me. She stepped out of her nice car and looked like she was from the old Prell Shampoo commercial. Her hair bounced in slow motion as she moved and gently fell around her shoulders. She was fresh and clean. My head was throbbing from the stiches and I was penniless in a shelter. "She thinks she is going to talk to me," I thought. "What could she possibly know what it is like to be me?" She sat down at the table with me smiling and enthusiastic. I felt irritated. I finally asked her, "What the f--- could she possibly know about me?" She quietly said, "I know what it is like to be you. I was right where you are now once." I do not know why this hit me so hard that this beautiful fresh and clean woman could relate to me! She told me more about her. My advocate was a college student! I was amazed and my very thought at that moment was, if she can do it—I can do it! I am going to college! I got a job and found a room to rent once I left the shelter. I knew I wanted to take us back home to Minnesota, back to the Ojibwe, and find that home where the wind did not blow through.

I had 17 roommates. In Boulder, you do not live alone in an apartment or house, you rent rooms in other people's houses. We got a room with a working fireplace! I loved my job at Senor Miguel's Mexican restaurant, and I bought an old bicycle to get to work, dropping my daughter off at childcare and sometimes bringing her to work as the Mexican Restaurant, being family-orientated, allowed for that. She loved it and got to have Shirley Temples as I waited tables. I made $1.01 an hour and $100.00 a day in tips as I was in, "the richest county of Colorado." Life was feeling good. Half of my 17 roommates were strippers at the Bust Stop and tried to get me to dance with them and work at the Bust Stop. We would practice dancing to Michael Jackson's Thriller album. They made in one day what took me a week to make waitressing. At that time, I met an Italian man who took to me and my daughter like we were long lost family. He loved us and was very protective of us. Was he a person who cared for us or was he sent by the Creator? He told me if he caught me in that place, he would kick my a---! He meant it. He said, "So how would you feel if you're buying an ice cream for your *daughter and some guy comes up to you and says, you look different with clothes on?" I stuck with my job at the Mexican restaurant. I made it; I was ready to go home! I finally proved to myself I could make it!*

> I remember the kitchen of this large house. I ate carrots from the fridge and cottage cheese all day long. They were fresh and cold. I tried roller skates in the front of the house on the sidewalk. I danced in the kitchen and laughed with the people. I traveled riding on a bicycle my mom pedaled with wind in my hair. I sat long hours at the Mexican restaurant at the bar drinking Shirley Temples and eating cherries. I knew I belonged. I was always home.

Before I left, I had one more experience with my abusive boyfriend who I felt was an ex-boyfriend, but he did not think the same as me. My daughter was playing with kids in a home where they loved my daughter. I was close by in a cabin hanging out with my boyfriend and a male friend. Food was always scarce, so when we found a large can of tuna, we were excited. We found an opener and 3 forks and began eating. My boyfriend refused to eat so it was our friend and me eating. He watched us for a while and then he jumped up and started strangling me. He was very strong, a former bull fighter. I could not fight him. He strangled me and I felt myself going down. I could not breathe, knowing he was killing me and knowing he was going to bury me out in this desert behind the cabin as we had traveled to New Mexico for a few days. I seemed to be aware he had killed two women before. I seemed to know things like the people who love my daughter would gladly keep her. Her mom just disappeared. I was horrified at how easy a person can kill you. I was going to die! Then, in this very remote area, a car came down the dirt road out of nowhere. A car! He stopped strangling me and ran to the window to see who was driving by. Was that a coincidence or did the Creator send that car? He never returned to finish strangling me. I grabbed my daughter out of that house and made it back to Boulder. It took me years to talk about this or mention his name because I thought I would call him to me. I got a second chance. I needed to get back to Minnesota. I remembered what that emergency room doctor said. He tried to warn me. Again, I was so grateful to the very helpful people who helped me get home, or did the Creator send them?

I had a blue silky coat that was given to me. The coat was fluffy, warm and beautiful adorned with subtle flowers imprinted. There is a picture that exists with a man standing on an empty road. He is wearing shorts with a bandanna on his head. He is holding a staff out with his right hand. These seemingly unrelated items are connected. They are my comfort and my fear. The coat was given to me from the couple as I sat in their home while my mother almost died at the hands of this man in the picture. I remember him. His name. His picture. I do not remember him hurting my mother. I remember the fear and knowing he should never find us.

Back home in Minnesota, back to Ojibwe country, back to family and friends and to Lake Superior! Colorado being so dry, I had a new appreciation for growing up around water! We stayed with my sister for a while and finally rented our own apartment. We sat in it with a candle on a soup can lid as it was all we had, but we were so happy! I told my daughter the lullaby I had spoken to her all along, this is home, still touching my heart. We were home! For a while, we still walked to the soup kitchens to eat as it took a while to get enough food in the cupboards. We would walk from the West End to Union Gospel Mission to eat like it was nothing to walk that far! It took some time to transition to an apartment from being homeless. I signed up for college in the American Indian Mental Health Training Project at the University of Minnesota, Duluth. If my advocate could do it, I could do it! There I met all the spiritual people of that era who were guiding this project. I met Jimmy Jackson, a well-known medicine man in Ojibwe Country, who told us to always offer tobacco even during hard times because you do not know where that journey is going to take you or what gifts come from that hard journey. All the people who helped me and my little girl or were sent by the Creator, I was so grateful for. I appreciate the gifts that came from enduring those hard times and especially the second chance at life. My lullaby, "Mama is right here, this is home!"

I walked the hallways of the University looking at the tumors in jars at the medical school, hung out in the Anishinaabe club, watched the stars in the planetarium, fell in love with the library, books, copier machines that required dimes to copy, and scanning the microfiche. I knew I would go to college before I was 6 years old. Most of my short life, I lived with little material things. I had a list of adverse childhood experiences, but I had the one thing that research cannot fully account for in resiliency factors. I had one person, my mother, that sang a new soothing reality into existence. She sang me safe in the darkness and shined light on the beauty of the world. She sang praise into my soul and reminded me what really matters. She breathed a chorus of gentle lullabies with stories of new beginnings and cycles breaking. She transformed what many see as despair into repair. She was planting seeds that no one noticed buried in that darkness.

At night in my own apartment sleeping in cheap beds we found at a rummage sale, I would put my head in the pillow and just be terrified for us being in Boulder, Colorado. I could not do it there as these emotions would not help us survive, but for a while, I could allow myself to have all the emotions about being homeless at a time where I was safe, and my daughter slept peacefully in the other room. I also have made many blankets over the years and have given them away. I hope that makes up for the blanket I had to steal. I felt the need to give back, and through my education, I later became a domestic abuse advocate and national/international trainer.

Yes, we were homeless, but it was never our identity. When you see people who are homeless, it is a temporary situation that we have no idea where it is going to take us. You are seeing people in transition like sitting in a bus station, and maybe you will be pulled in to help. Will it be because you care or did the Creator send you? Do not give up on us. Was my daughter negatively affected by being homeless? I can tell you that we got an apartment just in time for her to start kindergarten. The first day all the kids were crying and hanging on to their parent(s) legs screaming, "Don't go, don't leave me here!" My daughter was calmly sitting at a table looking around. She said, "So, what are we going to do here?" I could see her confidence and strength. We survived together! She was a survivor where this was just another situation and hopefully it would be a pleasant one. I knew my lullaby would change now: "Mama is here for you and will always be by your side! "

Mazinigwaaso (She Sews Beads)
Kit Rohrbach

I sit
where my grandmother sat
where her grandmother sat
one green glass bead
another
another
a leaf begins to grow
beneath my needle

in the center
a not quite perfect rose
red and pink
red and pink

one glass bead
another
another
falls between the floorboards
joins its fellows
that my grandmother
     her grandmother
               dropped

Anishinaabe women
sewing here

Autumn Afternoon Walk
Diana Randolph

Agate
Liz Minette

is a glacier scream

a cut that knows
mastodons

she has a river face

she's horse-shaped w/

a genie in her
pocket

a witch who carries

roses.

From Sky to Shore
Gregory Opstad

after Barrie Brown, From Sky to Shore,
11" x 12" x 6" kiln glass

I found my home in a fine arts gallery, the exact image
of a place I once lived. A sandy shore, blue water,
whitecaps melting into the sky, cattails in the foreground.
Wait. Not cattails. Sawgrass. There are no cattails here.

The arms of Siskiwit Bay reach out to the lake, the arms
drawing the water in. And the waves . . .

The artist has walked along my beach, she follows
my footsteps, along the path from the cabin hidden
somewhere up in the woods. She walks the lakeshore
where Lost Creek meets Superior. I take this walk
each day, morning coffee spilling as I stumble
on uneven sand. Would the artist spill hers as well?

My father built this place when his world became simpler,
a place for my mother and him to live out their days.
And she did but he walked here until he could walk
no longer and had to leave.

My children played on this beach, ran in the surf, had bonfires
just this side of the grass. They brought their children here,
taught them sand and sun, about horseflies, gulls, and water.

Across the water, the clouds come down to meet the lake . . .

She has been here many times, this artist, breathed the same
morning air, watched the same birds sweep over the bay.
I wonder if she would like to borrow my jacket; the sun
hasn't yet warmed the day. Soon the sand will burn her feet,
flies will worry her ankles. For now, she and I wait, reflecting.
The realtor is coming to pierce the ground with his sign.

Pain Before Glory
Matthew Tillman

In life some people have it good, and some people have it bad. As for me it was a painful journey growing up. There were a lot of ups and a lot of downs in my life, but then there were times when it was just constantly down. I have come to learn that the thing about pain is it demands to be felt. My outlet to release my pain was the game of football.

Growing up in Pine Hills, a town in Orlando, Florida, I lived in a 1 story house with 12 siblings. Starting off things were pretty tough. My father was 18 and my mother was 16 when I was born. They were young with a teenage mindset, so they did not know how to be parents. My parents abandoned me; they left me at my grandparents' house with and went to live the fast life. My father was heavily in the drug world using and selling, so it was all about the hustle. There was not much time for him to raise a child let alone be a father to me. My mother was always on the go, partying, clubbing. She started selling her body in the streets to make a living, and she also was not there to raise me. Life was so tough being born into this world. It felt as if you were so much behind. I did not have any guidance or direction. I was left to learn all of that on my own. It was very painful growing up. I knew nothing about genuine love or what it felt like to have a mother or father or even to have a family that cared.

My grandparents are 50 years older than me, so our generations were very different. We had nothing in common. They were very laid back people that allowed me to do basically whatever I wanted to do. It was a good thing and a bad thing. I had no discipline or a set foundation. I could leave the house early in the morning and hang with the kids in the neighborhood all day long and come home when the street lights came on. That was dangerous too because it caused me to get in so much trouble at a very immature age. I started hanging with the older kids because I could learn from them. I was the type of child that would be ahead of the game, always quick on my feet. The older kids I would hang with began to show me different ways to hustle for money, obviously not the legal ways. This began to open doors that should have never been opened. I got into stealing things for money and drug activity. I continued to do things that I was not supposed to be doing. I was hanging around people that did not really care about because I was trying to fill a void that I was feeling that was never filled. At a young age, it was very painful for me where I was at. I did not know how to navigate through my pain.

I will never forget the first moment I went to my cousin's football practice. I stood along the side of the fence, and I remember seeing how much fun they were having out on the field. They were running around doing drills, and it made me so excited that I wanted to join in on the fun and decided to start playing football. I was so excited for my first practice. It was almost like being in a whole new world. I had nothing on my mind. It was like all my problems were away. The only thing that I was focused on was learning and playing the game of football. I could let everything that I had inside of me, the pain, the anger, the feeling of rejection out on the field.

Football started making a big difference in my life and I could tell because there was a change in my attitude. I started to feel what family felt like. I even started learning key values of what life was all about. I learned what accountability was, because I could not let my team down based on my actions at practice or during a game. In high school I had a few stumbles and roadblocks. My past tried to come and haunt me. The friends that I used to hang with in the streets thought I was being fake because I was choosing a different lifestyle, a more positive lifestyle. I was getting called all kinds of names: fake, pretender, soft.

My parents said that my upbringing was not their fault. They left me with my grandparents so I should have grown up just fine. I still kept in touch with my parents, but we were not as close as normal kids my age are to their parents. The things that were being said to me started to play an effect in my life, so I started looking for love again. I became sexually active and more people wanted to hang with me because of my popularity from football.

It was almost like I was going backwards instead of forwards, going back to my past with the weekly parties, being on every scene that I could hang with girls. All of that was making me slowly lose focus to the point that I started skipping school. I was not doing any of my homework and was missing out on great opportunities. I lost my football scholarship to the University of Miami due to not being prepared and having things in order. I did not have a plan, and I let all the things around me distract me and take me away from the ultimate goal, which was playing football and letting that be my career.

Things were going downhill badly, which caused me to make

a decision on how the rest of my life was going to be. I had to put all my wants—partying, women—to the side and focus on my future. I will never forget what my high school football coach told me. He said, "Tillman, if you don't do it on the front end, you'll do it on the back end," which basically means if you do not handle your business like an adult the first time around, you are still going to have to do it later in life. It taught me to do everything right the first time to get it out the way. I remembered those words not too long ago, and that is when I decided to change my life. A friend of mine told me that a coach from a small college in Minnesota was coming to Orlando to work him out. He mentioned to me that since I was looking for a school to play football at that I should go to the workout and perform in front of the coach. I knew that my end goal was to go to college and pursue playing football, so I decided to take a chance and go to the workout, which really helped my chances. I did so well that the coach wanted me to come up and play for him, and this was the first step closer to my dream. I only played football in my hometown, and I knew that playing in Minnesota would have been different from where I was from, so I spent most of my time preparing to play and to leave my home.

When the day came for me to finally leave, I didn't know what to expect, but I had faith that great things were going to happen for me. I believe in God so I knew that he would only lead me down the right path. It felt so good being away from home and doing what I loved. It felt like everything that I went through brought me to this very moment. All I could do is just take in this moment. Every day is not easy. It takes a lot to want to grow. I made sure that I allowed myself to be uncomfortable so that way I could grow to where I wanted to be. What helps me is reminding myself that my comfort zone had to be disturbed to reach greatness. Something that I learned was how to embrace change better. Me moving far away from my home was really hard. It was the biggest change I had to do in my life. The more new situations in my life, the more I was required to change so that way I can achieve greater outcomes. Another thing that I learned was the more I challenged myself, the more I learned what is and isn't in my best interest. Even though I went through a lot growing up, I was able to play football which ended up teaching me a lot of lessons and granting me many different opportunities.

I surrender
Jamie Williams

It's dark, pitch black to be exact.
consuming my soul completely,
the reality is unknown. Who I've
become is what I've yearned.
No cares in the world. I am me.
The words of others, ignored,
Defensive is my only response.
The problem is theirs, blackness has consumed me.
This spirit is powerful. I cannot win.
Maybe they're right about my sin.
The needle pierces the skin and the
blood swirls. I know this is it.
I feel sick, lost in the dark.
You're my obsession. Control, I thought
I had. No, no, no, this is so bad. There is
nothing left of me. My spirit is broken.
This black spirit has taken control.
If it does not stop, my family will mourn.
I am a drug addict, I know for sure.
I surrender. I give it all to you, Gitchi Manido.

7 out of 8
Clair Friedman

Each night, I count my brothers.
& in the morning, when some do not survive to be counted,
I count the holes they leave.
Every unknown number that calls,
Every call that wakes me from my sleep
Did one of them die again?
Is that what it could be?
They didn't know it back then.
They didn't have anyone to tell them
inhaling fumes at the age of 12 from a pipe
with your father isn't right.
If only they'd had the guidance
I was lucky to have gotten,
I wouldn't be nervous to answer those calls in the middle of the
night.

I went to bed with eight.
When I woke in the morning, there were seven.
Another called me to break the news
while our dad was busy with the thing that sent his son to heaven.
My beautiful best friend was gone before I knew:
his brown, doe eyes and crooked nose
forever stuck in my mind.
Time went on and I still have seven,
but it's feeling more like five.

When all your older brothers do is heroin,
do you count them as alive?

Italicized lines from "dear white america" by Danez Smith

Don't Textbook Me
Denise Huckabee

Don't textbook me.
SEE me...

I am not some nameless client you read about in black and white.

I am living and breathing and feeling
and *Damnit-*
Get your nose out of that book and look me in the eyes...

I am not your latest science project to be observed like a rat in a cage.

I am human just like you-
Not some animate or inanimate object to be experimented on for your own curiosity or professional gain-
So *please*, put your microscope away...

I am not some soul-less statistic
to be entered into your national data base.

I think. I feel. I mend. I break-
I laugh and I cry and I love and I hate...

I am not some new or latest research-
For you to be applauded, and promoted,
or to earn you a substantial raise.

I am laughter and I am light-
I am passion and I am fight...

I am more than just your 9-5.
When you clock out I'll still be fighting to survive, so *PLEASE* leave me with more than just the ink you've memorized-
Dammit! *Look me in the eyes...*

And lastly,
I am not your pity project for you to belittle and psycho-analyze...with your textbook definitions and your $60 an hour plastic smile...

I am flesh and I am bone,
I am heart and I am soul-
And I am not so different than you, should life deal you the same
hand that *I've* been thrown...

I don't care about your certificates, licenses or degrees-
And your educated words do not at *ALL* impress me...

Come down to my level.
Sit a while with me in my pain.
Speak my language so I can *understand* you- and when I'm gone,
don't forget my name.

I may not have had the years of schooling
that you had to learn how to diagnose me-
But I promise that I will see right through you before you *ever* figure
out me...

Be real with me and don't lie.
See me through the lens of your heart *beyond* the information
stored up in your mind.

Don't textbook me.

Please...

SEE me.

Daisy Close-up
Diana Randolph

Dust on Your Skin
Tekla Stolberg

Dust on your skin.
Wax on your lips.
Down your chin it
Drips…
Drips….
Drips…..

You weren't born to be fair.
With dust on your skin
and pollen in your hair.
Show off those scars
to those who peek
under the soot
drawn on your cheeks.

Tear stains in dirt on flesh.
A flimsy armor on your chest.
One by one the cracks appear
For those who won't look in the mirror.

You were born perfect,
I'll have you know…
With all your cracks
and skin of snow.

It will take time for you to see
the way you appear to me.
An Angel who,
like the sun,
shines their love
on everyone.

Everyday
I'll have you know
I'll love you with all I can bestow.

Demons
Tekla Stolberg

You sleep in the dark.
Falling deep
into the inky black
demons waiting
to pull at your threads.
They'll unravel you
until there is nothing left.
There are no doubts that they cannot see.
Your lies will not help you here.
They will unravel and unravel,
leaving you to sew yourself back together
with morning's light.
They attack with your fears.
Try to guard them,
and they'll rip at your flesh.
They'll ruin you
from the inside out.

There was a man once
who struggled with demons.
They rotted him.
They left him with breath
like a jar of rotting flies,
and skin yellowed with jaundice,
his face covered with scars,
eyes worn with pain.

Those same demons may take you,
rotting you from the inside out.
Night after night unraveling you,
as your body lays in the ink.
Till the morning light
shines on your tears.

Ringed City
Elliott Crompton

Before the Fall
Dakota Burton

It's not illegal, she told herself. *There are no laws against it. Besides, you could use the company, all alone in this big old house. It's not illegal.*

Those words had been her mantra for the last week, while she was waiting for Biotech to deliver her order. Strictly speaking, she wasn't wrong. There was nothing illegal about what she had done. In fact, it was a trend now to buy Biotech merchandise. Their antibiotics had done wonders for the medical field, and their fire-resistant trees had done wonders for places such as California, Texas, even the Amazon. The company had a hand in so many fields, it was practically an empire all its own. It was their newest technology that had everyone buzzing, though they released it several years ago, and it was one of these "new" products that had Casey Blanc pacing the entrance hall of the mansion she had inherited from her late grandfather.

Her grandfather had raised her after her parents had died when she was nine. His wife had died a few years back, and he had been more than happy to have Casey come and liven up the old house. Her grandfather had been her best friend, and as her career began to take off and she became too busy for much of a social life, he became her only friend. At least, he had been until he died. There was nothing spectacular about his passing. The doctors said it was old age. Whatever the reason was, he was gone, and Casey was now alone in the world. Which was what brought her to this moment, waiting for her order to arrive.

Casey glanced at the clock. Half-past eleven. The delivery people should be arriving at any moment. Casey ran through the checklist in her head again to make sure she had everything the website had said she would need, and that she had done everything she had needed to do to prepare for this morning. She'd even remembered to take some time off from work so that she would be free in case any complications arose concerning her purchase. As she reached the end of her list, she half-giggled to herself, remembering the last task she had set for herself: *Panic*. Well, she had that one down pat. She was startled out of her thoughts by the ringing of the doorbell, followed by three sharp knocks. Obviously whoever was at the door wanted to make sure she knew they were there. She took a deep breath, then marched to the door.

There was a tall, thin woman on the other side of it, dressed in business attire. She looked more like a lawyer than a delivery woman, but one look at the person next to her confirmed that the woman was, in fact, here to deliver her Biotech purchase.

Casey had ordered a hybrid. A human-animal hybrid. Perhaps years ago this would have been seen as an unthinkable horror, but after gene-editing, nobody really got up-in-arms about anything anymore. Hybrids were actually becoming quite commonplace. Some families bought them as playmates for their children, others as companions. The term "companion" was sometimes used to suggest a certain type of companionship, but all Casey was interested in was someone to make the house seem not quite so empty and quiet. The website said male hybrids tended to be less temperamental than females, so she got a male. She also chose a cat hybrid, as they were more self-reliant than dogs or any of the rodent breeds, and she'd always liked cats.

There were no pictures on the site, so she didn't know what her hybrid would look like and looking at pictures of Norwegian Forest cats only got her so far. Even now that he was here in front of her, she wasn't able to get a good look at him, since the Biotech employee was impatiently asking for her signature and giving a rehearsed thank you speech for purchasing from the company. After the paperwork was in order and she was no longer needed, the well-dressed delivery woman took off, leaving Casey and her hybrid alone on the front steps.

Casey was now able to direct her attention solely to the cat hybrid in front of her. He was good-looking, in a soft, cute sort of way. His skin was pale, but not sickly, and he was slim. Casey would almost describe him sleek, though she knew he was probably much stronger than he looked. Maybe that was part of the cat genes? He had green eyes, with vertical pupils, definitely from the cat genes. A pair of black, velvety ears sat nestled in his ebony hair, pressed almost flat to his head. His tail, which was long, very fluffy, and the same color as his ears and hair, flicked nervously behind him.

Casey jerked, realizing her staring was making him uncomfortable, and stepped aside so he could enter the house.

"Uh, please, come in."

The cat hybrid did as he was bid, slowly, cautiously. Once he was in, Casey shut the door, and turned to see him scenting the air. She stood watching him for a moment, before calling out to him.

"How about we head to the living room? There are some things we should probably talk about."

He nodded and followed her down the hall to the aforementioned room. She gestured to one of the couches, inviting him to sit down. He did so tentatively, seemingly still wary even after she had told him it was okay for him to do so. His ears were nearly flat against his head, and he curled his tail around his waist as if trying to protect himself, though from what she had no idea. She sat on the couch opposite him, and gave him a warm, somewhat awkward smile, trying to make him feel more comfortable.

"Hi."

A beat. "Hello," he replied.

"I'm Casey." She moved to shake his hand but decided not to at the last second.

He nodded. "My new owner."

Casey shifted uncomfortably. "Well, yes. I mean, on paper I guess I am but..."

His ears lifted slightly, catching her eye for a split second before her gaze shot back down to meet his.

"I-I'd rather you not think of me that way."

His pupils dilated slightly from their previous slit shape, and his ears straightened completely. "How... how do you want me to think of you then?"

She shifted uncomfortably once again. "I... look, I know you were... I'm not looking for a pet just... a friend."

"A... friend?" At her nod, he gave her a half-smile. "That sounds... nice."

Casey smiled back, relieved. "Good. That's great. Uh, so, you know my name already, but I don't know yours."

The hybrid's ears flattened against his head again. "I don't have one."

"They didn't give you one at Biotech?"

He flinched slightly. "N-no. I had an ID code. NF-257."

Casey's eyes widened, her mouth falling open slightly. She quickly recovered, and in a tone of finality, said, "Well, here, you won't be a number. Wait here, I'll be right back."

She stood up and left the room, heading to the library. It was a big library, full of books that her grandfather had collected over the years, along with some of her own. She knew her way around the shelves quite well, so she knew exactly where to find the book she was looking for. In roughly three minutes she was back in the living room, the tome clutched in her hands.

She paused. "I don't mean to be rude, but can you read?"

He nodded. "They taught us everything from reading and writing to basic household chores. I love playing different instruments, but I wasn't allowed to use them outside of training."

The hybrid had started to smile as he spoke, but by the end of his sentence, it had disappeared. Casey frowned, but quickly wiped it away and replaced it with a bright smile.

"Well, I have a guitar you can use, if you'd like. If you want I can even get you your own."

His eyes widened and a smile broke out on his face, his ears and tail twitching excitedly. Casey's heart melted. "Really? My own guitar?"

"Yeah. I can order it later if you want." She then remembered the book in her hands. "Oh, here, I thought this might help with your, er, name situation."

She handed him the book, and he took it curiously, eyes scanning the cover. He gave her a glassy-eyed look. "Y-you're going to let me pick out my name?"

"Of course. I'd rather call you something you like, rather than a name you're forced to answer to."

A tear rolled down the hybrid's cheek before he wiped it away. "Thank you."

Casey gave him a warm smile. "You're welcome."

The next week was spent settling Luka, as he'd chosen to be called, into the house. Clothes were bought, a guitar was ordered, and plans were made to repaint one of the bedrooms to suit Luka's tastes. He'd chosen the bedroom across the hall from Casey, feeling more comfortable being where he could hear her. He insisted on helping her with the household chores and enjoyed simply being in the same room as she was. They spent many afternoons in her study or library; she would write or read while he would play his guitar. Sometimes they would just sit and talk. Casey did most of the talking at first, telling Luka about her job as an investigative reporter, her hobbies, and her grandfather. Luka liked hearing about him the most, and Casey loved to talk about the man who had meant so much to her for so long. Eventually, Luka began sharing as well. He didn't talk much about his past, but he talked a lot about the things he wanted to try, places he wanted to see. By the end of the first month, Luka had become a whole new person. He was still quiet; he didn't like to make a lot of noise, but he was very playful and affectionate. He loved to write silly little songs about whatever popped into his head. Oftentimes his songs were about something Casey had done that had amused him. Today though, there was no song, just lighthearted teasing.

"Coffee's in the microwave, Casey."

"I'm telling you it isn't! I just pulled it out, and now I can't find it."

"You never took it out. You opened the door, got distracted by your phone, then shut the door again without taking your coffee out. It's still in there." Luka was doing a fantastic job of schooling his facial features to look like he wasn't enjoying this immensely, but his tail gave him away, swishing excitedly back and forth.

"No it's not it's…" She trailed off as she opened the door, seeing her mug in the appliance. She glared at Luka, who smiled innocently at her.

"Shut up."

"I didn't say anything."

"You didn't have to. Your tail gave you away."

Luka jumped slightly, surprised, then glared playfully at his tail. "Traitor."

Casey burst into laughter, and Luka quickly followed, their combined sounds of joy drifting through the kitchen.

Life was pleasant for the two; however, there were still times when Luka seemed to struggle. With what, Casey wasn't sure, but she knew he'd open up when he was ready. He didn't like small spaces, and liked to leave his bedroom door open if he wasn't changing. Casey wasn't too fond of small spaces either and often left her own door open, a habit left over from living on her own for so long, so she thought nothing of this. There were things that sent up red flags in her mind, however. It didn't happen often, but once in awhile Luka would wake up from his naps gasping and covered in sweat. She imagined this happened at night as well, but he never said anything, so she couldn't be sure. He never liked being alone either, always insisting that he come with her whenever she had to leave the house. It could have been the Norwegian Forest cat DNA, as they were known to become quite attached to their owners, but the almost panicked behavior he would exhibit if he thought she was going to leave him alone made her worry. He also didn't like to talk about his time at Biotech, and whenever she brought it up, he would answer a few questions, but if she continued to press him, would shut down and retreat to his room.

A few months went by, and Casey and Luka were very close friends. After her vacation time was over, her job didn't leave her with much free time, so when she did have the odd day off, they took full advantage of it. Recently, they had taken to having movie marathons. They'd make a bunch of food and beverages, grab a dozen or so blankets and pillows to make a fort with, and spend the day losing themselves in other worlds. The first few marathons were Casey showing Luka all of the greats, including *Star Wars*, *Lord of the Rings*, *Harry Potter*, and *The Matrix* (though they both agreed the first movie of the trilogy was the only good one). Soon though, their binges turned into just talking about anything and everything while a movie played in the background. It was during one of these sessions that Luka revealed his biggest secret.

Casey had decided to try asking about Biotech again, perhaps Luka would be more open now that they were much closer. She made sure to keep her tone light, so as not to spook him.

"So, what was it like at Biotech? Was it like being in a movie? All of those scientists bustling around, making history?"

Luka was silent, and his ears were pressed flat to the top of his head, tail around his waist. Casey sat up and paused the movie, gently grabbing his hand and squeezing it. "Hey, what's wrong?"

Luka wavered, seemingly unsure, before speaking. "How much do you know about Biotech? Like really know?"

Casey's eyes widened. She knew from past interviews with informants what that phrase meant. "What are they doing?"

Luka curled further in on himself. "Nothing good. I don't remember much, they wipe you before you leave, but I guess that much pain can't be taken out by a machine."

A gasp, and Casey's arms wrapped around the hybrid's shaking form. They sat there for a few minutes, Luka quietly recounting what little he could remember of the horrors of the Biotech Hybrid facility.

"And the cages, there were so many, and all of them filled with other hybrids. Terrified. The place smelled of fear, pain. So much pain…" Luka broke into a heartbreaking mewl, his cat DNA taking over his human instincts.

Casey's mind was running faster than she ever could hope to go physically. An idea was forming, one that could either be the greatest one she had ever come up with, or could end with her lying in a ditch, if not something worse.

"Luka, I think I know what my next article is going to be." She gave the hybrid one more squeeze, then pulled him off the couch and towards her study.

"W-what are you…"

She turned towards him, a grin on her face. "We are going to make the empire fall."

Alice: Flowers
Mason Martin

Siri and Me
Peggy Trojan

I ask a lot of her.
Set the timer,
word definitions,
home remedies for bee stings,
the age of Robert Redford,
when do the Packers play.
When I thank her,
my daughter laughs and reminds me
there is no one there.
But Siri is so polite.
Once she said,
"I didn't quite get that."
I railed at her, letting
her know I didn't
finish my question.
She replied, "That's not very nice."

Poems Crowd My Mind
Peggy Trojan

Some, like young children,
jump up and down shouting,
"Look at me!"

Others, more mature,
whisper around my pillow at night
to remind me they are waiting.

Some, so old,
they remember mountains
opened by the light,
and my refusal to be a rock
for a hundred million years.

Life Skills
Jan Chronister

In fifth grade
we were assigned
a demonstration.
I showed the class
how to gift wrap a box—
a skill I've used a lot
over the years.

To earn a badge
in Girl Scouts
we learned to tuck
hospital corners on beds.

But nowhere along the way
did they prepare us
for the news that shakes our world
when mothers, sisters, aunts, and friends
receive a diagnosis no one wants to hear.

I see men in trucks alone,
wonder if they might
have a wife at home
who suffers, may soon die.

They drive around for a while,
then return to a life
requiring skills no class or club
ever taught us.

Nature Abhors a Vacuum
Jan Chronister

Hurricane's eye hungers
for houses to devour.
We set empty nets in lakes
again and again
until pulled up full.

I ask about you
at the powwow,
find out you died.
Did I speak your name too soon?
Will your spirit come
to fill the void?

I learn of another
who danced with death,
refuse to say his name.
Instead I call him
Fagan, a role he played on stage,
a man who taught homeless boys
to fill their empty pockets.

Judging Poems Submitted to a High School Contest
Jan Chronister

Students write of broken dishes,
mirrors, hearts, as if their lives
are over, as if they've already seen
wreckage, suicide, abuse.

Because they worked hard
on these poems, sent them in,
I suspect they already know
heartache, accept second best,
mourn a father killed by cancer.

Message X V
Marlene Wisuri

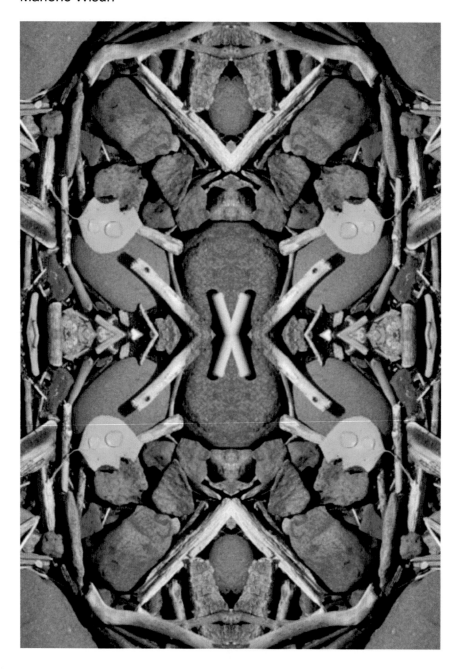

The Path of Totality
Marie Zhuikov

The problem with Justin Kincaid's eyes began on August 21, 2017. On a dusty hillside in Oregon, the curve of the moon's shoulder nudged away pieces of the sun. The crowd of people hurried to don their cardboard eclipse glasses. But to Justin, the sun still shone as whole and bright as ever.

Marjorie stood beside him. Through the background noise of the gathering, he heard her say, "It's a third of the way gone! Isn't that cool?"

Justin turned his head from the sky and flipped up his glasses. Marge's pale face was lifted to the sun like an offering. She drank in the last of the warmth. Her long red hair – noticeably oily these days – was swept back from her face, tendrils falling over her shoulders.

He flicked his glasses back on and looked up again. "Yeah, amazing!"

His heart beat a little faster. He hoped he sounded convincing. Why wasn't he seeing the eclipse? Something must be wrong with his vision. He rubbed his eyes behind the glasses.

This trip to the eclipse's path of totality had been his wife's idea. Marge said she needed a change of scenery. So they drove early on that August morning from Medford to Salem, Oregon. Craig and Betty, a young couple who had recently begun working at the bank Justin managed, stood beside them on the hillside.

The two couples had driven separately and arranged to meet at a rest stop along the way. As Marge and Justin approached the bathroom building, a woman pushing a stroller walked out, followed by her partner. Justin walked past but looked back to see Marge stopped outside, staring at the child. Her arms were crossed over her wrinkled shirt, her face stricken.

The parents glanced at Marge and hurried on. After a few moments, when Marge still wasn't moving, Justin sighed and went to her. He gently touched her arm.

"C'mon Marge. It's okay. Come inside."

She let herself be led into the building, turning back once to watch the retreating couple. With one hand on her elbow, Justin guided her to the women's restroom. He let her go and was relieved when she kept walking in on her own.

When Justin came out of the men's room, Marge was

already out, talking with Craig and Betty. After exchanging pleasantries, Craig left the women and took Justin aside. Looking down from his lean six-foot-four-inches, Craig said, "Is Marjorie okay?" He hesitated and then added, "She seems distracted and looks kind of . . . ."

Justin knew what it must have cost Craig to say this. In the short time they'd been working together, he'd noticed that Craig always tried to be positive, especially to his boss. Still, Justin was embarrassed that Marge's condition was so obvious.

"She's just having a rough go of things lately," Justin said. "Marge needed a change, and the eclipse is a good distraction. She's been looking forward to seeing it so she can tell her students. This funk is only temporary."

He didn't want Craig to know the real reason for Marge's mood. They weren't close enough friends for that.

Justin hoped Marge could return to her job as a substitute science teacher. It worried him that she didn't just bounce right back. He wasn't used to that.

Staying home gave her more time to dwell on things, which didn't seem productive. She used to like making elaborate desserts while listening to classic jazz. Now their home was silent and even the store-bought cookies were running low.

Justin pulled his thoughts to the present. Until he could figure out what was wrong with his eyes, he should probably offer some comment on the eclipse. "How far gone do you think it is now?"

"Oh, at least fifty percent!" The excitement in Marge's voice warmed something in him. She hadn't been enthused about anything in the past two months.

Justin took off his glasses and looked around at the scattered crowd to see if that helped his vision. Maybe his eclipse glasses weren't working. Maybe his retinas were already burned beyond repair. Everyone was rapt, looking up at the sky. He could see the people just fine.

Betty chirped, "It's getting darker."

Justin ran his hand nervously through his black hair. This eclipse spanned from Oregon on a path to South Carolina. Fourteen states in total darkness, the first time an eclipse covered such a wide swath of North America since 1918. How could it be that he wasn't seeing it?

Marge took off her glasses, too, and looked up the slope.

"Do you feel that? It's like a cold wind is blowing down the hill."

Justin *could* feel that. He could smell grit in the breeze. Was the light changing? Maybe. He might need to make an eye appointment. He put his glasses back on.

After more time passed, Craig said, "Ninety percent! Hey, look at the shadows on the ground – they're so sharp!"

The others moved their arms around, playing with the shadows.

"Oh my God, this is so weird!" Betty danced a bit in delight, her brown hair bobbing.

Marge tapped Justin's arm. "Look around, just try looking around!"

He couldn't escape. Lowering his head, he raised his glasses again. In the crowd, people were sharing glasses with those who didn't have any. Some wiped tears from their eyes at the wonder of the sky. Justin moved his arms and looked at the ground just for show. "That's so cool!"

But it wasn't. He saw the same sorts of shadows that accompanied him any day the sun was shining. Sweat trickled down his armpits while an emptiness grew within.

After a few minutes, a slow cheer began to rise from the crowd, as if they were all at a football game, the moon a player running for the end zone.

"What the . . .?!" Marge held her glasses with both hands.

Beside Betty, Craig said, "Oh my God! What is happening?!"

The crowd laughed and started to clap.

Marge pointed to the town below. "Look! The streetlights are coming on."

Now the cheers of the crowd gave way to widespread and indistinct exclamations. Justin could only assume people were seeing the luminous circle of light from the blocked sun. Dammit, why couldn't he see the corona?

Craig took off his glasses and the rest of their group followed suit. He pointed his in a long arc. "Look at the sunrise, it's in every direction!"

Justin looked around with everyone else, plastering an expression on his face that he hoped would pass for awe.

"I don't know what I expected," Betty said, "but it wasn't this! It poked a hole in the sky. It's so dark."

"This just looks so wrong! The sun really is coming up on every horizon. It's so incredibly beautiful..." Marge's laughter gave way to deep breathing. A few children in the crowd were shrieking in delight.

Now Craig pointed into the sky. "Look, it's Venus! I can see stars, too."

Justin heard crickets begin to chirp. Relieved that he could contribute something real, he mentioned the sound.

Marge spoke more softly than before. "Oh yes, I hear them, Justin. We are inside totality."

Totality didn't last long. Soon, Craig said, "There it is – the sun!"

Many in the crowd started to cheer and applaud. Everyone put on their glasses again.

For a few more moments, the group marveled at the sun's return – long enough for Justin to suspect the day must surely be as bright to everyone else as it had been to him the whole time.

The others started taking off their glasses. Justin removed his, too. "Let's eat, I'm starving," he said, desperate for a distraction.

The four walked over to their picnic basket and sat on a blanket they had spread out earlier. As he sat, Justin scanned the crowd and saw that they, too, were returning to their regular concerns, as if a spell had been broken. His heart began to slow.

Craig looked at his watch. "Well, if you guys leave soon, you could be home before dark." He gave a laugh. "Regular dark, that is."

Betty finished a bite of her sandwich. "This was so cool, I almost don't want to leave."

Marge sighed. "Me neither."

Justin thought about what awaited them – a four-hour drive with just the two of them in the car avoiding talk about anything meaningful, back to a silent house; back to a garage full of boxes they hadn't had a chance to move to the nursery.

When he came home from working late, sometimes he would find Marge standing in the dimness and dust, whispering the brand names like a mantra: "Graco DuetSoothe Swing, Modern Baby Nest Crib, Baby Bjorn Quilted Cotton Bouncer Bliss, Bristol Bassinette . . ." Other times, he'd find her sitting in the middle of the box pile, huddled as if in a womb herself.

Maybe they should stay on this hillside.

Marge continued, "I'm ready to get home. I don't know about you guys – I feel like someone flipped a reset switch inside me."

A bit of the old glow lit her eyes. She had already eaten half her sandwich and was eagerly opening a bag of potato chips. Justin was glad she seemed to have her appetite back and he hoped this lasted. Maybe the drive home wouldn't be so bad.

"I . . . we feel pretty great, too." Betty looked to Craig. "You want to tell them?"

Craig's smile was broad as he gazed at Marge and Justin. "We just found out and we'd like you to be the first to know – we're having a baby!"

In the moment it took Justin to respond, he remembered everything: the panic in Marge's eyes as her contractions started in bed. Even though they weren't sure what to expect with their first baby, they knew that at twenty weeks, those kinds of contractions were way too soon.

He rushed Marge to the emergency room where the doctors tried to stop her labor, but it was too late. Her pains came harder and faster.

An "insufficient cervix," they had called it. Andrew, their baby boy, had come too soon into a world that was too big and too cold.

On the hillside, Justin glanced at Marge before he spoke. She was looking away, her eyes focused on something in the distance.

"That's great, you guys!" Justin said. "You must be so excited."

All the hope he'd been feeling started to drain away. He said a little prayer: *Please let Marge be all right. Please.*

Betty bubbled, "Yes, a whole new world is opening up for us!"

Marge was still looking away. Justin said, "Hon, isn't that great for them? Hon?"

As if with great effort, Marge slowly turned back to the conversation. Her eyes glistened with moisture. "Yeah. Yeah, that's great. When are you due?"

"Next April," Betty said.

"That's my birthday month." Marge's voice was wistful.

"What day? Wouldn't that be great if it was the same?" Betty took an enthusiastic bite of her sandwich.

Marge took a deep breath and smiled. "Yeah, that would be cool. My birthday is the sixth."

After packing the remains of their lunch, the group sauntered to the bottom of the hill toward their cars.

Betty walked next to Justin. "You're awfully quiet," she said, peering at him. "What's up?"

"Just takin' it all in," Justin lied. "The eclipse and now this. It's big news. I wish you guys the best."

Promising to get together again soon, Craig and Betty climbed into their blue Honda to visit Craig's parents in Salem.

As Justin started the engine of their car and pulled out of the lot, Marge said, "Wasn't the eclipse awesome? I can't wait to tell the kids at school about it."

Cautious, Justin settled on, "Does that mean you feel like you could go back to work?"

"I think so. I feel so liberated." Marge gestured to the sky out the window. "I mean, if the sun can disappear and reappear, I ought to be able to deal with this and keep going." Her hand rested on her belly.

"I'm so happy to hear that." Justin patted Marge's leg as he turned the car onto the highway. "I was a little worried when Craig and Betty shared their big announcement."

As he drove, Justin visualized Andrew in his incubator, covered with an oxygen tent to help him breathe. His chest rose and fell in a quiet battle for air. Wires coiled around him like snakes.

"That was hard," Marge said. "But you know what? Life goes on. I can't keep wallowing. I'm stronger than that."

Justin gazed at Marge for a moment. "Damn right, you're strong. And I'll help."

He turned his attention to the car's speedometer. As he set the cruise control, he dared ask, "Do you think it would be helpful if we visited him?"

Marge didn't need to ask who he was talking about. Her eyes grew large and thoughtful. "I . . . I don't know." She hesitated. "Let's just go with this feeling for now and not rush things."

This was progress, finally. On the rest of their drive back to Medford, their conversation flowed much more easily than on the drive out. During the occasional silences, Justin thought about Andrew. Despite their parents' objections, he and Marge had decided against a funeral. They didn't want to spread the sadness around. Justin had taken care of the burial arrangements to spare Marge.

Andrew was buried in one of the local cemeteries – the one with the ponds where the ducks liked to swim. A friend said it was peaceful there, but Justin had never visited the grave. Neither had Marge. They didn't even put a headstone on it.

He could visualize the map that the cemetery lady had drawn for him – a red pencil line leading from the entrance to where Andrew was buried – the number of his metal grave marker written in the margin. Justin had filed it in the small cabinet in their home office.

During the following days, Justin's vision seemed all right, but in his dreams, he kept hearing an owl hooting, low and haunting. He wandered from room to room in his mind but couldn't find it. He'd wake to Marge shaking him, asking if he was all right.

Part of him knew the owl was Andrew, but he couldn't tell Marge what was wrong. She finally seemed like her old self. She started showering every day and her hair was clean and shiny again. She even went back to work. He didn't want to mess that up.

He, on the other hand, dragged himself out of bed every weekday morning. On the weekends, he slept until 10:30 a.m., which was unusual.

After a few weeks of this, he came home on a Friday night to find candles on the table and dinner waiting. Benny Goodman's clarinet music wafted from the speakers. He laughed in delight, not brave enough to ask about the occasion.

Their conversation was easy through dinner. Marge waited until dessert to ask, "What's wrong, Justin? I'm worried about you."

Justin slowly chewed the homemade turtle cheesecake for a while, letting the caramel melt on his tongue. He thought back to the nightmares. "I think it's Andrew."

"What about him?"

Justin rubbed his hands over his eyes. "I think we need to visit his grave."

Marge hid her face in a fall of her hair. She swept it aside.

He reached across the table for her hand.

She took his hand in hers.

*

Saturday dawned clear and warm. They stopped at a flower shop to buy a spray of baby's breath and blue irises. With Justin driving and Marge consulting the red pencil line on the map, they drove under the cemetery's arched gate.

Justin maneuvered slowly down the narrow asphalt paths between headstones. They passed a pond with white geese and green-headed mallards clustered along the shore. A few people walked their dogs among the headstones and a maintenance man drove a riding lawnmower on a hillside.

They reached a big Douglas fir growing in the center of a turning circle. Marge pointed to the side of the road. "This looks like it. Let's park here."

She climbed out of the car and led the way, still holding the map. Justin followed, carrying the flowers, the musky scent of the baby's breath hovering around him. His free hand shook slightly.

He remembered how the nurses let them hold Andrew. He looked so peaceful, his bluish lips and eyes closed, his featherweight body so still. Justin had peeled off a few squares of monitor foam tape that were still stuck to Andrew's thin parchment skin as silent tears flowed down his face. Those were the only tears he'd shed. After that, it was like they dried up.

Marge looked up from the map at a spot on the lawn where the earth had been disturbed between two large headstones. "Is that it?"

They walked over and Marge bent down, feeling the soil for the small round marker. She brushed dirt away and looked up at Justin. "Yes, it's the same number." Then she sat back and stared at the impersonal silver marker glinting in the sun.

Justin dropped to his knees beside her. He peered at the marker and laid the flowers beside it. He turned to Marge. "You okay?"

Tears glistened on her cheeks. "No."

Justin sat and put his arm around her shoulders.

The two of them started rocking side to side. Justin felt a liquid bubble rise through his heart. Slowly, it continued upward through his throat and into his head where it burst, releasing all the sorrow and loss he'd been pushing aside for so long. He choked back a sob.

"It's okay." Marge's voice was shaking. "You need to feel it, too."

They both cried all their tears. Wiping his eyes, Justin noticed a new sheen to everything, as if a film had been washed away. The grass was greener. The flowers on the graves more colorful. The air was crystalline, like after a summer rain.

As he blinked to test his new vision, his mind flashed back to the eclipse. With each blink, he saw the sun as it should have been on that hillside in Salem, blocked by the moon. Blink by blink, chunks of it disappeared.

He kept his eyes closed longer. In fast-motion, pinpricks of stars appeared as the eclipse blocked the light and then allowed it to return. He fought dizziness as a replay of multiple sunrises beamed from every direction.

Sitting by the grave, Justin could finally see what everyone else had on that dusty hillside in Salem, Oregon. Blazing orange and deep purple light washed over the dark behind his eyes, as if a hundred smokeless wildfires burned on the horizon. He gasped.

Marge asked, "What's wrong? Is something wrong with your eyes?"

Justin opened his eyes and turned to Marge, smiling and holding her. The physical contact steadied him.

After a long moment, he replied, "No, my love. I see more clearly than I have in weeks."

Dedicated to my parents, who I wish had visited the grave.

Harbor Beacon
Elliott Crompton

The Deep Blue Sea
Francis Hadley

The expanse of endless water left my sugar-fueled toddler form silent and still. For what felt like hours, I stood there as the white foamy waves licked the sand like an ice cream cone. Deep in my Goldfish stuffed tummy, a knot of something grew, a need to run. Yet I stayed, caught between a desire to never look back or to dive headfirst into the depths forever.

Three-year-olds don't think about much other than right in front of them at any given moment. Why was the camera stuck into the webbing behind my mom's seat? Why couldn't I play with it? Why did daddy look so sleepy? This was the endless game my parents were losing as we wound along the rocky shores of the Delaware Bay. Finally I sat, silent, strapped into my too itchy car seat as it gulped up my small form, watching the clouds float by. My body could not raise my head above the edge of the window even straining against my restraints, so most of the time in the car I spent cloud gazing, watching the white forms darken and bubble as a storm approached or simply reaching my small fist towards the airy beings that resembled my mother's sewing box that got me spanked for touching without asking.

When we pulled into a parking spot, I was released from my polyester netting, and carrying with my bright yellow sand pail, I made my way to the sandy stretch of land called the "beach." That pail never felt the grainy sand fill its space, however, as my time was taken up by another task. Before me stretched a large blue expanse as far as my small eyes could perceive. It stretched out its endless arms to beckon me to come closer. And I did, slowly, towards the damp, salty form. I took it slow; I didn't want to risk scaring it.

Despite the short time I had been alive, adventure came naturally to me. Scaling the fabric lined mountains of our sofa, or viewing the horizon of my kitchen spread out before me in chrome when I reached the top of our refrigerator. Child's play compared to the dwarfing nature of what stood in front of me. The roar of its anger filled me with indifference. I felt every inch of my small form wash over me. The water had been long before me and would continue to be well after I was gone. That's when the knot began to twist in my gut, forming a feeling alien to me.

Water did not make me afraid. In fact, I very much enjoyed

the first time every night where I got to coat my parents in bathwater while seeing how long my rubber duck could hold his breath. How long could I hold my breath, if the waves grasped me and performed the same test? My water came from a bathtub. Or a garden hose, with that strange metallic tinge that came along with it. Not the mass of dark blue lounging before me, sunning itself, taunting me.

The dry sand gathered up around my soft legs had yet to fully form as I gauged the distance between myself and my foe. My short legs twitched, ready to sprint for the safety of my mother if this monster decided to make any sudden moves. Then, much to my horror, my mother picked me up and carried me to the beast. My wailing did little to change her mind as she plunged me knee deep into the water. At first the unending crash of the waves knocked me around, but soon I found my footing. I retreated a bit, where the flow softened, but my mother insisted I remain. The water felt comfortable, if not a little cold. It wrapped my feet in a blanket of care not even my rubber duck could. My feet sank into the soft muck below as the curly grasses tickled the back of my knees. Without realizing it, giggles bubbled out of me at the multitude of sensations.

Again, the idea of the liquid closing over my head, taking me away from all of this to a land of enchantment, came over me. I considered it, completing my baptism and leaving this world behind. All for a chance at something unknown. In the end, I scuttled up the beach back to my Nickelodeon towel and to the safety of what I knew. But I watched with curiosity, wondering what life under the water held for me. Swimming through the cooling tides, never having to worry if I would miss the next episode of Blue's Clues. Swallowed up by a fish whose scales catch the light shining through the waves who gets devoured by a creature I cannot begin to fathom. At my age, I had no idea what that meant, but I understood that if I entered the water again, I would lose myself in the foamy bubbles, until I melted away and settled onto the sandy floor.

I returned to that beach several more times before we traded crab cakes of Delaware for cheese curds in Northern Wisconsin. My parent's marriage wasn't so lucky. While I grew to have a distant respect for the sea and all it held, I never again heard the song from that first experience. Standing on the shores of two of the Great Lakes gave an echo of that feeling, like hearing the ocean trapped in a seashell. Something woke in me as my feet squelched in the soft sand beneath the waves. Something that causes my heart to jitter when I've been in a place too long. Like agitated water, I always push forward, trying to find that feeling I felt so long ago.

My Black Garbage Bag: Life in the System
Tricia Gottschalk

The first foster home I went to was with my god family. I was only 7 years old. At my god family's house, I would get in trouble for not cleaning the rooms like they wanted. If I didn't pick up the clothes or garbage how they wanted me to, I would have to stand in the corner for hours, and if I were to move, time was added on to that. I would run from them when I could and when they caught me, I was spanked with a spatula.

I ran from them a lot because I didn't like how they treated me. When I ran, I would hide in the slides in the local park that was close to their house or I'd run to someone else's house. They never really cared for me or worried where I was at until something wasn't done right that they wanted done. Then they would come looking for me.

After some time, I was taken from their house and placed in the shelter for a while. I didn't like the shelter. I had to sleep in a room by myself because I was the only girl there. I didn't like that I was locked in a room by myself. Just to be able to use the bathroom at night I would have to knock on the door so the staff could let me out. When I arrived there, I didn't have any clothes. I would have to wear the staff's shirt to bed so that they could wash the only clothes I had every night. At least they were clean and ready for me to wear the next day.

One day, my social worker came to pick me up from the shelter. The shelter staff placed a few things they brought for me in a black garbage bag and handed it to my social worker. She walked me to the car and helped me in it, then brought me to my next placement. It was with my relatives. They had four boys. I had to sleep on the floor downstairs where it was cold and scary, and I didn't really eat much. They had very little food. When we would eat, it was always white rice, some type of red sauce, and hamburger. At Easter, the four boys got Easter baskets, but I didn't.

During this time, school was very difficult for me. I got into fights with my friends and other students. I even got into fights with teachers and staff members. I ran from the teachers who tried to help me, and I also cussed at them and threw things. I just didn't trust anyone.

After about six months with my relatives, the cops came to the school to get me. At the office, there were two cops waiting for me. They walked me to the car and helped me inside. I looked over and saw my black garbage bag in the seat next to me. At that moment I knew I was being taken from my relatives. On the ride all I could think about was "What did I do wrong? Why didn't they want me anymore? Why didn't I get to say goodbye?"

The car ride didn't last very long. They took me back to the shelter again. One of the officers walked me to the door carrying my black garbage bag of clothes. I really didn't want to sleep alone in a dark room again. When I was alone, I would think about things like "Why does no body want me? Am I really that bad of a kid? Should I better myself?" I mean I was only 9. What 9-year-old has to worry about where they will end up again and why no one can love them?

After a while, my social worker came to pick me up again and there was the black garbage bag. We walked out and she placed me into her car, threw my bag in the back, and we drove off. The ride felt like it took forever to get to the next home. I pictured where I would be next, if there kids my age, and if it would be a fun family. When we finally arrived at a house in Barnum, there was a man standing in the driveway. As I got out of the car with my social worker, he came up to me and said, "Hi. My name is Ralph." I remember being shy, but I believe I said hi back.

My social worker handed Ralph my black garbage bag and walked us into the house. There was a woman who greeted me when we walked in. Her name was Dawn. Dawn showed me around the house and where I would be sleeping. I saw that I would have a bed and I would be sharing a room with others. I was happy I wouldn't be sleeping alone. I didn't like the dark. There were toys in a toy box and Dawn said they were for everyone to share. I couldn't believe that they had toys I could play with.

After all that, Ralph took me to the local grocery store and let me pick out some things I would eat. There was so much food in the cart that I asked if I should put some back or if he had enough money for all of that. I've never seen so much food at one time before. He told me not to worry about how much food he was buying or all the money he was spending. All I could do was worry because I was underfed.

When we got home, I went into the house and Dawn called me to go upstairs. When I got upstairs, she was folding my clothes and putting them into piles to be put away. She also had a peanut butter and jelly sandwich with chips waiting for me. So, I ate that and soon enough the other kids were coming home from school and into the house. They all introduced who they were, and I told them who I was. Ralph told me I would be staying with them for a while.

Once a week my case manager came to ask me how things were going. I'd always tell him that I liked it here and that I liked playing with all the kids. I would call him the candy man because every time he would come to check in, he would bring me candy.

When summer rolled around, I got some money to buy some summer clothes and shoes because I didn't have anything. This was the first time I got to spend money how I wanted. Instead of buying all clothes, I bought a pink suitcase so that if I was taken from this home at least I'd have something other than a black garbage bag to put my clothes in. So that I would look less like a foster kid.

One day, I got off the school bus and saw that Ralph had bought me a bike. It was purple with light blue strips and streamers on the handlebars. I couldn't believe that it was all mine. It was brand new too. I've never had anything given to me that was brand new. I thanked Ralph and gave him a hug. I was so happy with that bike. I rode it for hours and all over. It didn't matter if it was raining, cold, windy, hot, or cold. It never ever stopped me.

I had lots of freedom that summer. I met my first best friend. Her name was Mackenzie. She was my neighbor at the time. We would bike to the park and play until it was just about sundown. Ralph would take us swimming at the lake and I would have sleepovers. We would play baby dolls and house. My first Christmas with Dawn and Ralph I couldn't believe how many gifts I got. I was always used to getting nothing or, at most, just one gift.

Then in July of 2006, Dawn and Ralph went to court to sign off on being my permanent legal guardians. They came home, sat me down, and told me that I would be living with them forever. I was filled with joy and excitement. I have never been so happy in my life because I loved my family and I loved where I was at.

That black garbage bag has taught me a lot in life. It taught me that even when you have very little with you and other people have given up on you, there will always be a family that will be grateful to have you. That family will love you like you are their own. Ralph has taught me to respect everyone and everything, to be patient and know good things will come and for that, I will be forever grateful for my dad.

Sibling of an Only Child
Lisa Poje Angelos

I am the woodland sister
that breathes through the leaves
and places the notes of birds
on the staff of memory

I reach my hand straight
to the heart with the subtlety
of moss carpets, the surprise
of a hopping toad, a profusion
of tiny white flowers

Who but a sister can give
you this confidence?
Who can say "step onto the log"
and leave you knowing despite
the length and curve and fear
you will not fall?

I am the woodland sister
that speaks through the soles of
your feet with pine needle duff;
through your hands with the
textures of bark

I etch our stories right
onto the soul with the intensity
of fierce wind, the sorrow of a
bird fallen from the nest, a gift
of ripe blackberries

Beside you, within you
I guide you, my sister
amongst the trees or city streets
we walk our steps together

Pursuing the Fire
Lisa Poje Angelos

Life stacks up pain
like cord wood and
we must all decide
whether we will
let it moulder--
accumulate, disintegrate us
Or, if we will find
a way to burn it;
to use it with a purpose--
Cover our bodies in the
soot and wash it all away
Spark imagination, insight
Thaw our deepest corners
Throw light into our future

Alice: Mad Hatter and Hare
Mason Martin

Willa Goes for a Walk and Falls into a Hole
Sara Sha

As the setting sun melted the woods into a syrupy haze, Willa realized she would have to spend the night here, in this hole. If anyone realized tonight that she was missing, they wouldn't be able to find her. They would find her car in the garage, her purse on a chair.

The absurdity of her situation made her laugh in disbelief. A regular day, like so many regular days, had turned into an unusual day, an extraordinary day. All she had needed was a little fresh air and exercise before dark. She'd thrown on a light jacket, grabbed her water bottle from the kitchen counter, tucked her phone into her pocket, assuming there was ample battery life left, and had headed out into the warm autumn evening.

And now, maybe just a short hour later, she was in a hole, in the woods, right on the edge of town. There were cars passing by on the road only a few hundred feet away, a drug store just beyond that. This was a forest she walked in almost every weekend for ten, twenty, maybe even thirty years. This was a friendly forest; she'd never felt threatened by people, wildlife, or even a malfunction of her own aging body. "How can this be happening?" she whispered to the night air.

The dirt stirred up from her attempts to climb out coated her tongue and nasal passages and she wiped her face on the sleeve of her jacket. With more optimism than was warranted, she checked for phone for life, but it was cold and dead. She silently cursed herself again for not leaving the house with a fully charged phone. She vowed she would never, ever do that again. Ever. She sat down on the hard ground and zipped her jacket up to her chin. She was getting sleepy but she didn't dare lose herself to sleep. Safety was in awakeness. She could better defend herself if she was awake and heard something coming, and with that thought she picked up her water bottle in readiness to use a weapon. But fear was in awakeness, too. The more tired she became, the more her imagination played with her.

She felt fear take hold as the last traces of light diminished. What kind of creatures came out at night in the woods? What kind of creatures burrowed out of the earth and would be sharing this space with her? Creatures with fur on their backs and wiggly naked legs that she wouldn't be able to see, only feel. What if a deer or a badger or a bear fell into the hole on their nightly wanderings? Or worse, what if something supernatural flowed through the forest at night like a low-lying fog, eventually pouring into the hole like a misty waterfall, slowly consuming her very spirit, crushing her soul, smothering her human breath, and painfully, excruciatingly turning her into something else?

She buried her face in her arms to avoid looking up, terrified of what could be looking over the edge at her. She imagined pasty white faces with long, pointed teeth looking down at her, laughing at her, leaving her to only imagine what they would do with her.

Would it be embarrassing to die of fright in a hole right in her hometown? They would find her body, unharmed (hopefully), but the life gone. All of her plans and aspirations would disappear with her last breath; her baking supplies, her books, her canning jars, sitting there only to be given away or auctioned off.

Why did she decide to walk to this hiking trail rather than drive? If her car was parked in the lot, they'd find her rather quickly.

She blamed the chocolate. She'd eaten a lot of chocolate that day. For some reason chocolate was everywhere. A coworker brought in brownies, a customer brought in cookies, her friend gave her a thank you gift of a Toblerone, her neighbor dropped off chocolate chips muffins. All in one day.

She sleepily wondered about that now. Why was there so much all at once? She had read that cacao was sacred in some cultures and that it was used in ancient ceremony, but she'd forgotten the details. As her eyelids grew heavy she imagined all of her consumption was preparation for a sacrificial ceremony. She had unwittingly bowed to the forces that encouraged her to fill herself with cacao, then she had headed for the forest, winding her way through streets and sidewalks and up a steep hill to get here, just for the sake of adding steps to her tracker, so she thought at the time. And now in the darkness, the ceremony would start. Did she hear drum beats? The beats came from a darkness coiled deep in the earth, the pulse of the earth calling out the dark creatures that lived in the night, and they crawled out of fallen trees and out from under the stickiness of stones, all slithering, limping, dragging themselves toward the hole where she was, the drumming getting louder and louder.

She jerked herself awake and realized it was only the drumming of her own heart in her ears. The earth slowly became silent again.

But then her heart's drumming started again as she heard footsteps in the leaves not far from her. Was it someone looking for her? Did someone realize she was missing and did they know she needed to walk off a belly full of chocolate and decided to climb the hill to work it off? Or was it a teenager escaping a hellish home and came up to the hill to get away? They could have a nice talk, sitting on a rock overlooking the town, they could share stories and cigarettes and the teenager would go back home feeling better about life.

The footsteps stopped, then pounced. Definitely some kind of predator, maybe a fox, Willa thought. The thought of a fox warmed her heart. Foxes were cute and sweet and were depicted on children's toys. She would be okay, she told herself. All of the sounds were just the maternal night woods freeing herself from the human tramplings of the day, allowing herself to return to her own rhythms and activities. Fox would hunt mice, deer would eat whatever they ate, owls would hoot and turn their heads in full circles.

She woke gradually, then with a start. It was still dark in the hole, but the sky showed promise of eventual light. She immediately remembered her predicament and felt hungry, thirsty, and she had to pee. She had no choice but to pee in here. She walked the few feet over to the other side of the hole, pulled down her pants, and let a stream of warm, strong-smelling urine into the dirt, the pee steaming as it left her body. She felt like she was marking her territory and wished she had thought of that last night. She could have peed around the circumference of the hole, letting everyone know this was her turf and they should keep away.

She shook off the residual pee as best she could by bouncing up and down, then pulled her pants back up, rearranged her clothing comfortably, then went back to her resting spot. In her overtired mind, she imagined this to be her bedroom, over a couple of feet was the living room, she'd already delineated the bathroom. But there was no room for a kitchen. And nothing to find in the kitchen if there was one. She mentally divided the living room in half and made room for a tiny kitchen. She put her water bottle there and then took a sip of water, put the bottle down, then took the small steps to the living room. She would have to think of a plan today to save herself. Today was Sunday and it wasn't unusual for her to be incommunicado on a Sunday. Likely no one would be looking for her until tomorrow, when she didn't show up for work.

Part One of her plan was that she would listen to anything that sounded like someone on the trail several yards from the hole and would yell for help only then, to save on her voice. Part Two, she would try to figure out a way to climb out. She would not, could not be stuck in this hole.

The sunlight rose over the rocks and spilled dappled light into the forest, sending shards of smoky light into the hole. Willa was able to see chunks of root and rock embedded in the sides of the hole. This was promising. If she strategically chipped away at the hard dirt in places where the roots and rocks were, she could create a ladder and climb right out. She would climb out, walk back to the trail, go down the hill, and go home. She would have the whole afternoon to rest, to eat, to drink. She'd call her sister Ruth and laugh about her folly, of seeing a loose dog, a cute black dog with a white-tipped tail, and leaving the trail to catch it and falling into a hole. If only she didn't love dogs so much.

As she tried to dig out a foothold in the hard soil above a large root, she realized creating this ladder of life would take longer than she thought. Her fingers strained trying to pick away, poke, and scrape, and she made a small hole, not even big enough for the tip of her toe. She scraped at the hard wall, her fingernails and fingerprints getting jammed with dirt, and she became wary of bleeding. It would do her no good to bleed right now. Injury was not an option. After having no success with the first toehold after several minutes, she rested and took a tiny sip of water. She would need a tool.

She looked at her metal water bottle. It would make a great digging tool if she could just break it open. But as she stomped on it, it would skitter and ricochet about the floor of the hole, beautifully indestructible, just as it was advertised.

She pulled her phone out of her shirt. She'd hoped having the phone against the warmth of her skin would somehow revive it, but the screen was black and unresponsive. She now had in her hands the world's most expensive trowel.

Before she could continue, she froze. She heard distant footsteps. They were faint, but they were rhythmic. They had to belong to a human.

"Hello out there," she called out and suddenly felt foolish. She was a middle-aged woman in a hole in the forest. She must look desperate, a look she'd avoided all her life. She took pride in being strong, capable, self-sufficient, and fiercely independent.

Maybe it was her two bitter divorces, the untimely deaths of her parents, friends who moved away and were never heard from again; all desertions that made her determine long ago that people were undependable. People left her life no matter how much she loved them, no matter how much she needed them.

And she had to admit, maybe some of that was projection. She was a terrible friend, forgetting birthdays, not making coffee dates. She often simply turned her ringer off for hours for no reason, or would hide if someone knocked on the door. Sometimes she didn't like the inconvenience of other people in her life, with their interruptions, their needs, the responsibility of being available for them if they needed her, even for joyful camaraderie.

Goddess, she prayed, if a person can prove reliable and trustworthy and help me out of this hole, I will be a better friend. I will show up on their doorstep when they are crying, I will do something special for their birthdays, I will bring them gift baskets for no reason at all, I will send them texts just to let them know I am thinking of them.

Because she needed human help now. There was no way to get around it. Maybe this was a lesson she needed to learn, to be shown the error in her ways. We were put on this earth to build community, not spend excessive amounts of time reading crime novels or binge watching television with knitting needles and a glass of wine.

The footsteps grew louder and she yelled louder, and then they grew faint and Willa visualized the forest walker deeply involved in their music or podcast, earbuds covering the teeny holes that would help her out of this one.

She sat on the ground and took another sip of water and as she realized this was the last of it, she felt her whole body droop. She would have to yell sparingly or she would get too thirsty and not be able to yell at all.

The rounded edges of her cellphone made her expensive trowel not a particular efficient one, but as she rested after carving a few indents, she felt hopeful. The sun was directly overhead as she finished what she hoped was another toehold. It was taking her much longer than she thought, but if nothing else, it kept her mind occupied and away from her predicament.

She decided to try out her ladder and see how it was working, and to her bitter disappointment, she realized she couldn't climb far. She kept falling off. And she just wasn't able to make holes big enough to hold any of her weight, and the one hole that was big enough, crumbled into a tiny avalanche onto the ground. She tried to get a running start, but the hole wasn't big enough to get a decent one. And the hole was too big to be able to brace herself by reaching another side.

Fuck the diggers of this fucking hole, she thought in fury. Who the fuck dug it and why? And fuck that stupid dog that led her here in the first place, then didn't have the decency to turn back and see if she was okay, or do that Lassie shit and run for help.

"FUUUUUUUCK!" she screamed. She flung her phone across the hole and she felt hope drain out of her. She didn't care who heard her, she didn't care if she wore out her vocal chords, she didn't care that her water was gone. "FUCK! FUCK! FUCK!"

It felt good. "FUCK YOU HOLE! FUCK FUCK FUCK YOU!"

She imagined the hills ringing with reverberations of this wonderful word, its delicious four letters bouncing around the cliffs then dancing down the hill to anyone and everyone working in their yards, or walking their fucking dogs. She imagined the beautiful word weaving through the trees and causing hikers to take out their fucking ear buds to hear it.

And they all would say, "What a beautiful word that is? I wonder where it's coming from?" And they would follow the colorful effervescence the word left behind and find Willa in this hole and they would also say the word and would create a beautiful human chain and pull her out of this fucking hole.

And she would punch each of them in the face and say "FUCK YOU" to each and every one of them for taking so fucking long to find her and help her.

She stopped yelling and savored this thought, and decided her situation confirmed her previous hypothesis that people were unreliable. As the sky turned pink, then purple, she realized that again, no one was going to save her and she hated them for it.

She lay on her back and watched the sky grow darker and she waited for her terror to come, but it didn't. She imagined herself as just part of the floor of this hole; she was part of the dirt, the trees, the air. She had nothing to fear because she was part of it all. At one point she saw the silhouette of a rabbit stop at the edge of the hole and look in.

"Send for help," she whispered to it, but she knew it wouldn't. And she didn't blame the rabbit because the rabbit didn't comprehend what she was asking. Rabbits were pure and good, just like the leaves and the grasses and the clean, damp night air.

She watched the blackness of night flow over, in, and around her and she let herself turn black and then watched the pinpoints of stars appear and grow brighter, just as she imagined her eyes, ears, nose, mouth, anus, vagina all become part of the stars. Her pores opened up and filled with light and she shone like the quarter moon nestled in the black tree branches reaching into the night sky.

She didn't remember sleeping. She watched the sky turn from black to indigo to gray to blue to yellow and loved the sky. She was tired and stiff, but she sat up and did some slow yoga moves that she remembered from a class long ago. She was pretty sure it was Monday. Today they would realize she was missing and they would look for her. Would her coworkers be concerned enough to act? She hoped so. She was always on time, rarely sick. They needed her at work and would notice immediately that she wasn't there. They would try calling her cell phone and there would be no answer. Maybe one of them would try to reach her sister and her sister would definitely be alarmed that no one knew where she was. She would take the police to her home and they would find her car, her purse. It would be strange, so they would start to look for her.

"Where were some places your sister went?" they would ask.

"She mostly went to work and to Target, but she loved walking in the woods," her sister would answer, and point up the hill.

They would have a dog smell her clothes from the hamper and the dog would clamber out of the police car and into the woods. The dog would leave the trail, wind through the underbrush and birch and would look down at her in the hole, barking and wagging its tail.

The vision was so strong, Willa's heart raced as she watched for the dog to show up.

But she eventually grew tired of waiting for the dog, and her heart slowed down. As the sky clouded over and the wind began to blow, she gave in to despair. But not completely. She let a piece of her be alert to the sound of footsteps, dogs barking, shit, even a drone.

She looked at the clouds filling up the sky and thought about all of the times she'd come here. So often she fled here to escape her usual disillusionment with her life, a disillusionment that walks in the forest helped relieve. Not that her life was bad, not by any stretch. It's just that she craved some kind of release from the day to day and she just couldn't find it. She worked; she did good work, really. But the hours were long, the data entry work tedious and dull, and it left her tired by the end of the day. She felt a sense of jealousy when she'd meet someone new and they would talk about their work like it was an extension of who they were. Willa's work was only a means to pay the bills and she was bored. She wanted to be around art or history or crime solving or cabinetry or small engine repair. She thought about changing jobs, but at her age, she needed to just dig in her heels and ride it out.

So she often headed for the woods and would always feel better. The oaks, the birches, the poplars, and the other trees she couldn't identify took her in and sucked the despair and guilt out of her and she would leave the forest feeling okay.

But the despair in her now, even as she was nestled in by the roots, the guts, the lifeblood of these same trees, wasn't releasing.

Was there purpose in all of this? The work, the cooking, the driving, the reading, the drinking, the thinking, the searching, the reaching? Did people have missions to fulfill on this earth? She thought of the people that had died in her life. Her cousin killed in a car crash when they were in their teens, the grandmother that slipped away in her sleep after an illness, her uncle who died alone doing a crossword puzzle. In the in-between time, between breathing those last breaths and the moving to the great beyond, was there a conversation? "This is why you were here and you've done well. Thank you." Then they would move to the light, disappear in the ether, or whatever happened next. Or was their light simply distinguished and their bodies burned or slipped into holes?

Like the hole she was in now. She hadn't considered it to be a grave, but as she gave in to tears, she began to think it might be.

Could her life end this way? She wasn't near done. She had fresh chicken in the refrigerator she needed to cook up before it went bad. She had applied at a pet rescue organization to adopt a dog just a few days ago. She was planning a road trip with her sister, she had just renewed her public radio membership, she had just purchased a new houseplant. It was absolutely ridiculous that she would die now in this hole. It made no sense whatsoever.

But she imagined as her cousin lay trapped in his car's mangled wreckage in his own growing pool of blood, he thought the same thing, as did a woman diagnosed with stage four breast cancer, as did the man who clutched his chest after climbing off a step stool to change a light bulb, as did the teenager who got caught up in the wrong crowd and now had a knife at his throat.

She stood up and marched weakly in place to warm up. As her blood flowed, she took stock of her situation, which was simple enough. She was in a hole. She decided to try climbing out again, using every last bit of her waning energy. She jumped as high as she could, then grabbed for something, anything, but landed with fists dusty from dirt. She clawed at the side of the hole above her, planning to build a staircase, but those plans were quickly abandoned as the dirt was well packed and wouldn't surrender.

She watched the gray sky turn dark again and sat down. She was chilled. Her water was long gone. Certainly the police dog would be here soon. She buried her head in her arms and listened and waited. The rain came and softly tapped her shoulder, startling her. Then she realized it was rain, and she laughed. "Oh why not?" she said and looked up, letting it wet her face, and she licked it off her lips. She crawled over to the kitchen area of the hole, and unscrewed the cap from her water bottle in hope of capturing just a little, just enough so she could yell again.

The rain brought out new sounds in the forest. It sounded like tap dancing, then like a beginner on a drum kit, then it gave into static as the rain poured down. The rain came into the hole at an angle, so Willa would shift her position to stay as dry as she could. But the wind would shift often and she gave up, curling herself into a ball to try to stay as warm as she could. The rains poured, then let up as if taking a breath, then poured again. The winds forced the treetops to scrape their branches ferociously across the sky and the sky would roar in protest with thunderclaps that would explode against the rock and send rolling echoes across the town below. Meanwhile in the forest, the leaves scooped up the rain, sending water down the tree trunks in tiny rivulets, seeping into the soil at their feet, wakening and refreshing the mosses, the fungi, and the humus. Creek beds gasped with activity as they filled their banks, leaping to life with spatters and splashes; shiny rocks appearing, then disappearing in the violent, velvety black current.

Eventually a morning sun rose, slowly dissolving the clouds, turning the remaining water droplets on the leaves into diamonds. The greens of the forest were invigorated and the animals slowly emerged from their hiding places, looking for a meal in the soggy leaves; the birds feasting on seeds that had shaken free from their pods and shells.

Willa went to open her eyes, but they were already open. She was surprised that she could see everything and she couldn't explain how this was, nor did she feel the need to do so. She could see all around her at the same time, the sky, the trees, the rocky ledges in the high places, the mushrooms in the damp places, the beetles in the underbrush. She was free from the hole and the giant wind was her breath as she inhaled the must, the dust, the traces of feather and skin, and exhaled great bursts of breath that made the ripples in the grasses and made dead leaves skitter and cartwheel down the hills. She ran her fingers through the treetops with affection and smiled as finches darted around and through her. The sun grew warm and she could feel the coolness of night give way to a toasty, comforting warmth on her gray, rocky face. She marveled at the streams and creeks running through the forest and it was her very blood running joyfully and spotlessly through her. She flapped her raven wings as she flew over the woods, over the road, over the neighborhood where she saw through her raven eyes police cars gathered and people milling about. She let out a huge sigh and she forgot everything, the tasks, the hole, the chicken in the refrigerator. She was the sun, spreading herself over the land, giving light to darkness, warmth to the shivering, and love to everyone.

Evening Glow
Diana Randolph

Echoes
Laura Krueger-Kochmann

unclear
and unbearable
searching for the answer
when I can't see myself

I close my eyes
and my bat self takes flight
I am comfortable in the night

buzzing of mosquitoes
scent of green
my wings alive to the air
its messages revealed to flexible finger bones
a freedom to swoop and glide
and hide
fly in black sky
and cry
my call to the world

and its answer guides me
I skim the water's surface and collect a drop

Summer
Laura Krueger-Kochmann

I

the first day of summer
my daughter and I take a walk
and pick dandelions
a bunch of bright and happy
to celebrate our freedom

yellow and smiling in the face of those who would call them weeds
        they grow like weeds
darting among their white-haired elders
who are content to appreciate the potential

of a small brown seed
carried on the wind by a bit of fluff
maybe just a few steps away
        maybe miles
to multiply

we take them home
and my daughter feeds some to her bunny
who nibbles the petals
munches on sunshine

II

in the middle of warmer days
we find a small speck
on a milkweed leaf
and out comes a hungry little caterpillar

we feed and feed its voracious appetite
until that fat, striped body hangs and curls in preparation
metamorphosis is so quiet
if you turn away for a moment
you'll miss the silent emergence

the two of us say good-bye to our beautiful monarch
in a field of wildflowers
delicate wind-rider
her wings fluttering
        change can be beautiful

III

savoring every moment of summer's end
we gather around the dying embers of a campfire
prolonging our goodnights

we talk of the gray jays that descended upon us earlier
camp robbers
in search of food
delighted by my daughter's spilled Cheerios

she wonders if they will visit tomorrow
after we pack up and leave for home
what do we leave behind?

Grace
Jim Springett

the little bit (two inches wide) of ivory
Laura Krueger-Kochmann

I

the card catalog
once dust-covered in the library basement
and dragged to the dumpster
now sits as a showpiece of the sophisticated bibliophile
yearning for another time
when wooden drawers
led the way to hours of good company

II

nearing a book's end, I hesitate
slow down to savor those last pages
like saying good-bye to a friend
and when those dear friends return in sequels
        (or rereading)
I am comforted by their company once again
the togetherness of real and imagined

III

I can—and do— carry all of Jane Austen's novels in one electronic
device
her words embossed on the cover
        "nobody minds having what is too good for them"
they are not heavy
but simulate something substantial
words
that resonate with countless readers
generate love, tears, adaptation
and fan fiction, the highest form of flattery

IV

two hundred years later, Jane Austen
we gather, a few of us
to read your entire beloved novel aloud

in one weekend
our link to you
real and imagined

It was Just a Bat
Deborah Rasmussen

I saved one once
in a house
from a woman with a broom.
Caught it with care.
Released it outside.
No great feat. Still —
something.

This is not to brag.
I just wonder how many
somethings
are at large in the world
and what the doing of them
could maybe do.

In the Beginning
Deborah Rasmussen

Coffee grounds cozy up
to all those empty peels
banana, orange —
my kitchen debris
becoming soil.

How many plates did god scrape
 to make the earth
        to make us
    out of egg shells, apple cores
        and a handful of stardust?

I toss a handful of sawdust
into the bin
turn it
breathe the fragrance of fresh dirt
turn it
listen to the slow rumble
of creation.

Choices
Deborah Rasmussen

> *Poll: 7 in 10 Americans say this election*
> *is the most important of their lifetime*
> *November, 2020*

In the next room voices argue the odds:
this state breaking, that state breaking
for one side or the other. So much is broken.
I carry my fear to the window, desperate
to be rid of it. Let the wind worry
for a while, let trees bear the weight
of waiting. Beyond the pane deer gather –
food scarce now, frost hovering, spring far away
but it will come, they say. *Believe.*
In such times, faith is the only answer.

A New Day
Jim Springett

How to Cure Sorrow
(And Why You Shouldn't)
Bradley Limanen

Have you ever wanted to rid yourself of the sadness you feel? Despite everything you have, and how good the world looks for you, do you still feel lonely, angry, lost, panicked? It's a normal feeling to have, and a necessary one as well. Without sorrow, we wouldn't be who we are. It is part of our survival, our ties to family and friends, and at times, drives us to do wonderous things that shape our world for the betterment of all.

If you still aren't convinced, let me tell you a cautionary tale, that, like the people it follows, has nearly been forgotten by everybody.

When the Goddess Aclea, and her God and Goddess brothers and sisters created Dostornia from the remains of a barren island, she filled every last corner of it with plants, animals, and people. From the common Humans, Elves, Caninefolk, Birdfolk, and Ancients that roamed on almost every part of the island to even the Turtlefolk and Fishfolk of the waters, the Ledopteron and Deerfolk of the forests, the Mammothfolk of the hills, and Dragonfolk of the skies. Unfortunately, she created monsters by mistake as well: Goblinoids, Kobolds, Orcs, Oozes, Evil Dragons, and other monstrosities that hampered the development of the people. It was common for the Gods to interfere with the struggles of the people, in their favor. While this saved them in the short-term, the people remained cavemen, essentially, there was no development into what they are now. And so, Aclea made a hard choice. She gathered up all her brothers and sisters and forbid them from tampering with the lives of the people.

Aclea couldn't play by her own rules, though. She knew that her people would just need to be nudged in the right direction. She had a plan to fulfill this…On a day long behind us, she went out onto the mortal world of Dostornia, and searched for people who met her criteria. They had to be smart, strong, kind, dedicated, and determined. When she found them, she would coax them into following her to a location far out of the reach of their brethren. There, she blessed them. No matter the race, the gender, they were transformed into fantastical versions of themselves…The Spirit People.

Spirit People were special; they could be any of the races Aclea created, with key differences. They had a proper and complex language. They knew how to make things that mortals could only dream of. Overall, they appeared much more evolved. They were essentially Demigods! Physically, they resembled Mortals. The only key difference were the markings on their bodies, specific to whichever race they were. These markings glowed at times, usually when they were in a positive mood.

Aclea transformed hundreds of people into Spirit People. Once she was finished, she gave them a mission to fulfill throughout their lifetimes. "I instruct you to go out into the places where mortals do not venture: the Deep Woods, the Tundra to the North, the Bottom of the Lakes, the Volcano, and Eagle Mountain. There, you will construct cities for yourselves, out of their reach, where you will practice and develop the skills and technology, destined to be taught to the mortals below. You will come out from your homes periodically to teach them what you have mastered, beginning with things like basic farming, monster defense, and hunting. Teach them until they have mastered these skills, as you have been born with. As you develop alongside them, keep teaching them new things, one step at a time." Those were her instructions, and the Spirit People followed them to a tee.

They created their new homes: strongholds in the Delta Tundra, complexes in the deep woods of the Hollow Marsh, temples within Mosaic Desert, the Bottom of Lake Dostornia, remote islands off to the West, everywhere out of reach of most mortals. Their buildings were constructed from the materials readily available to them in the environments where they settled.

And just as Aclea had instructed them, the Spirit People went to the homes of the mortals, sometimes once every few days, every few weeks during bad times, and every day during good times. The mortals were not scared when the Spirit People came to their caves and crude homes. They were intrigued by these new and somewhat familiar people. Spirit People of certain races would most often visit tribes and villages of the matching race, but even when this did not happen, the mortals accepted them. In their early stages, mortals were taught things that Spirit People were made masters of, like language, farming, and defense. But one of the most important lessons given was about sharing stories, and the power that it had to inspire and educate.

When it was time for them to leave for a while and make

sure the mortals practiced on their own, the Spirit People would go back to their homes and hone skills that they themselves had not mastered yet. This was an intention of Aclea, to create a people who had the flaws and ambitions of her mortal creations, while also being there to learn ahead of and teach the mortals. Wherever mortals were in their development, Spirit People were a few steps ahead. By the time mortals had mastered the first skills, Spirit People were creating schools, libraries, and establishing a government. One important thing they experimented with was magic. To keep their way of life secret from the mortal world, one thing they did was cover their cities with magical veils that kept the Spirit People and their practices hidden. It was unknown what would happen if a mortal did come across these places, whether on purpose or by accident. No records of such experiences have ever been made, which could mean a few things...

Some time had passed, and mortals were more widespread than ever. They had succeeded in creating villages and towns across the island, in all its various biomes. Meanwhile, the Spirit People had become so advanced that they were beginning to dabble in machinery and odd technologies. But still, they had not mastered magic.

Their standard of living was extremely high; most lived in comfort. Medicine was readily available. Almost no monsters would dare to challenge them. They had tamed wild beasts and bred them into fantastical new forms. They had started to create machines to do work for them. But there was still one flaw that someone saw in them. The Spirit People's Leader, King, Chief, Ogima, Boss, Big Kahuna, whatever you might call him, saw that despite their standard of living being so high, there was still sorrow in his people. They were in great numbers, but he saw that there were still people who were lonely. They had conquered the world, but there were still people who were lost. They were always safe, but he saw that there were people who were still panicked. There was plenty of food, but he saw that people were still hungry and desperate. There was peace among all of them, but he saw that people were still angry.

Everyone should be happy, why are we all still so sad? He thought one day. *There must be some way to rid ourselves of sorrow.* But how do you expel sadness from the body? *Magic, that must be the answer,* he thought. The Leader sent letters to every settlement of the Spirit People, requesting their finest mages to assist in curing them of a sickness that plagued their people. Believing that the Leader knew what he was doing, many accepted, and traveled out to the capital in the Delta Tundra, to work on the cure for Sorrow. It wasn't easy; it took years for them to figure out the logistics and uses of magic. Along the way, they learned how to write and use spells, create magical items, and enchant their tools and tech. Unfortunately, some of the mages went down darker paths in their pursuit, trying out unethical magics in search of the cure.

Through much trial and error, and a whole lot of elbow grease, a ritual was formulated, one that would help them reach enlightenment, pure happiness. And by this point, they had mastered magic, and knew how it all worked. A notice was sent out to every settlement across the land, letting them know that they must come to the capital in the Delta Tundra for the ritual. While most believed that their sorrows would be cured, there were a few who fled in response, believing that this ritual would bring more harm than good to their lives. The next day, in the earliest hours of morning, every Spirit Person from every corner of the island arrived. The mages began their ritual, starting with an incantation, then a sacrifice. When that step was complete, something began to boil out of the people's bodies…Blackish-purple shadows began to drip off the skin like water droplets off of everybody present, then coalesce into multiple masses that slithered out of the city and into the wilderness like a pack of snakes. The ritual…had been a success?

The people were overjoyed at first, cheering and celebrating all over the city. For a short time, they felt that there was no need to be sad, angry, or scared. This joyfulness was not to last, however. You see, it is impossible to rid yourself of emotion, just like how nobody can truly conquer death. The only thing that the ritual had done was rid them of the *energy* brought forth by negative emotion. You remember those shadows that left the people when the ritual finished? That was pure, raw energy. Emotion brings energy. I don't think anybody would dare to disagree. And there is an important rule about energy that needs to be kept in mind: energy cannot be created nor destroyed. *So where did all that negative energy go?* you might ask. What happened next, nobody saw coming.

While some Spirit People began the trek back to their homes elsewhere in Dostornia, many stayed behind to enjoy the festivities that had been planned for today. Celebrations of joy soon turned into horror as unknown monsters began to spill their way into the city any way they could, and negative emotions flooded back into their souls! All that negative energy that was discarded had managed to manifest itself as new monsters, ones that could not be fought off by the Spirit People anymore! These horrible shadow monsters embodied the negative emotions that they attempted to purge.

Lonesomeness and Panic pursued those who were far from their homes or confused and scared in the moment! Hunger chased those who were willing to do anything to save their lives, no matter the cost! Guilt sought out the mages and the Leader who formulated the ritual, now seeing the grave mistake they had made! And Anger ravaged those who were enraged that the cure had failed and brought something worse upon them!

The Spirit People were powerless to stop these hideous nightmare creatures. All the energy was gone from their souls and being used against them. Gone overnight were the Spirit People of the Delta Tundra. And the next day, the monsters moved on to every Spirit People settlement or temple they could find. Within a few days, they were all gone. All the people of this once great civilization were killed off by the products of their own hubris.

The plan to end sorrow was kept a secret from mortals. After centuries of the Spirit People coming to teach them things, they one day stopped coming. The mortals were rightfully confused, unsure what had happened. They tried everything that they could think of to try and coax them back out, announcing their mastery of the most recent skills they had been taught. Eventually, mortals began to notice things that haven't always been there. Mysterious creatures had been sighted all over Dostornia, the shadow monsters. They weren't so quick to attack mortals, however; for their emotions were still intact. Only the most broken and insane mortals could be preyed upon by them. The sudden disappearance of their friends and the appearance of the shadow monsters led the mortals to the conclusion that something had happened to them, and they needed to know what was causing it.

A last resort plan was formulated—going out into the wilderness and looking for the Spirit People themselves. The mortal's finest foresters, fishers, hunters, and warriors made long treks into the places where nobody ever came back from. Deep into the wilds, they found massive structures they did not recognize. The veils that kept the Spirit People's homes hidden had vanished over time, as the magic that kept them there had dissipated. The structures were empty, and nature was starting to take over again.

The mortals did not leave empty-handed, however. They brought back with them the relics and artifacts of that fallen civilization: magic items, spell scrolls, arcane focuses. They were intrigued, but they had no idea what any of these things meant. They had no idea what they did or how they are to be used. Mortals also took into mind the robotic remnants they found in those ruins, hoping to find out what their purpose was as well and if they were somehow also related to magic.

So, for the last many centuries, that's exactly what they've been doing. They've been trying to crack the code on magic and technology. And while they've made great progress, obtaining magic in a multitude of ways, they still haven't figured it all out quite yet; but they've had some help. Other mortals from across the seas to the East have come to the region, like Dwarves and Whalefolk: peaceful explorers who had also been dabbling in magic. Their current knowledge doesn't measure up to what the Spirit People knew, however.

But sadly, no Spirit People will be around to teach them that anymore. Their structures lay abandoned, now inhabited by monsters and other flora and fauna, their way of life could never be told, their existence has faded out of memory.

And that, my friends, is the tale of the Spirit People's tragic end. Because an entire race of people could not deal with their own emotions, there are more monsters in the world. And their people, now extinct.

So, the next time you feel like the burden of your emotions is more than you can handle, remember this story. If you can overcome your emotions naturally, taking your time to breathe, and make peace with yourself, you are better than these demigods ever were, who thought they could rise above their mortal traits, only to succeed, but at the same time, fail.

Calvin & Hobbs: Han & Chewie
Mason Martin

Aftermath
Meridel Kahl

Duluth, MN, July 21, 2016

Last night thunder shook
the ground beneath the house
rattled cups and saucers
plates and bowls
as lightning fluttered
like bolts of white silk
unraveling across black velvet.
Wild winds tore a giant section
of maple from its base
hurled it to the ground
tangled it through cedars and birches,
blocking front lawn, sidewalk and street.

Venerable trees
felled in half an hour
one hot summer night
will be sawed, stacked on curbs
for the city to discard.

We'll find our voices midst the loss
tell our stories to each other
and move through

as Earth spins, orbits
waves break, recede
as stars stand steady
in late July skies.

The Motor Queens
Maggie Kazel
        -For Dawn

Hot pink pedal pushers
long dangle earrings
tan bodied gal on yellow moped,
I am the flier of the sidestreets.

Hoots and howls
from all my girlfriends
and watch out, bitch!
from small minded big boys.

Rock 'n roll
fuels my ride
and best of all
are the curbside five,
six and seven year
rainbow girls
who flag their arms,
widen their eyes and mouths
Oh! Queen of the Road!
Motorcycle Mama!

I wave back grand
I wave back all
their devotion
all their surprise
Yes, you can! Yes, you will!
You are the motor queens
of my heart!
Speeding! Speeding!

Red Dress
Lucy Tyrrell

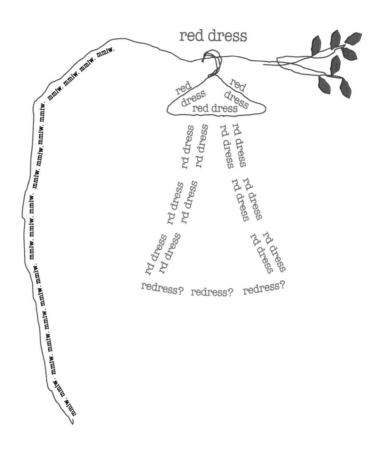

When Wildness
Lucy Tyrrell

When
pausing
at purple
lake reflecting
ink bowl etched in white,
I see soft ripple-wake—
beaver swimming through starlight.

When
skiing
at dusk,
I distinguish
feathered shape crouched
waiting in high-branch tangle—
owl eyes, round brown, watchful.

When
sensing
I should turn,
I find a form
curled tight at the base
of gray-barked spruce—
burnished-copper fox sleeps.

When
she stares
from willows,
I look behind me,
does she look beyond?
No, piercing eyes on me—
locked gaze, then wolf slips away.

When
wildness
touches me,
I melt in delight
for things ephemeral,
moments that vaporize like wisps
of sea smoke above a lake on new cold day.

In Translation on Safari
Lucy Tyrrell

In translation, words can run afoul.
Swahili uses sounds and pitch for meaning—
just like consonants with different vowel
give English words a brand-new leaning.

In his rudimentary Swahili,
the traveler asks Masai for help with jeep.
He speaks words, does not know them really—
he requests without the right inflection-leap.

The jeep is stuck, the axle wound with stems.
He asks Masai to please clear *nyasi* (nay-ah-si).
But what he speaks is not what he intends—
he has told Masai to drain *gesi* (gay-ee-si).

So, English speaker on his grand safari
hasn't fixed his problem with the grass.
And, surely, he can't travel very far—he
no longer has the engine fuel, the gas.

Coming Out
Susan Rees

Thirsty plants imbibe warm love in gentle sun,
drink their fill of rain. A robin chirps, a chickadee
sings "Here Petey," to choral burps of amphibian
procreation. Tender grasses poke through straw.
Dandelions wave yellow faces.

In a grove of aging elm and graying birch, buds
on dull black limbs glow red and gold, give birth
to leaves, lambent green against blue sky, while
fragrant scents tease flitting bugs.

Below its giant neighbors, one small maple waits
for chance to grow, bides its time for sweetened flow,
for bulge of buds on naked tree, for jolt of life from
deep inside, for shiny leaves with surge of spring.

On its naked limbs, where nascent leaves confined,
stayed safe from winter's cold, rising bumps begin
to crack, then open wide. Natal leaves unfurl. They
come out wrinkled, brown, drooping down.

Small maple cries, stretches out from underneath
its neighbors, tries to touch the sky. Crinkled leaves
turn smooth, then bright green. Reaching up, they
glisten proud in vibrant dance with life.

One God
Jim Springett

The Quiet Place
Rilla Anne DeBot Opelt

Angie sat on the overturned tombstone, her mind adrift while she soaked in the afternoon's autumn sun. She wanted to listen to the quiet and rustling of the last few yellow, red-brown leaves as they clung to the nearly bare branches.

She closed her eyes and listened very carefully for every rustle, every breeze, clearing her mind of all else. Then she heard a different, unfamiliar sound. She opened her eyes to look around the small, deserted cemetery. Time had stopped here. The graves, those that still had stones, were over 100 years old. It appeared to have been abandoned long ago. The path that lead to it had once been a dirt road. She'd discovered this place years before, when she was a little girl, exploring her new hometown. She'd never told anyone about it. She had always enjoyed it, coming here to find the peace missing from her young life. Now, as an adult, she came when she needed solitude, time to think. She referred to it, in her mind, as her Quiet Place. It had always helped, somehow, to come here.

She was watching a squirrel run among the tilting gravestones, then scoot up the nearest tree when a horse-drawn wagon came into view. It was turning into the narrow, dirt road leading into the cemetery. A big man, dressed in a dark brown suit and broad-brimmed brown hat, handled the reins easily as he guided the horses into the small clearing. The woman sitting beside him was hunched under a grey-blue shawl, her face hidden by a bonnet of dark, somber grey.

Soon another wagon came into view. The couple riding on the seat were silent. They, too, wore dark, dull-colored clothing. In all there were five wagons, each stopping to form a line behind the first. No voices were audible. Just the noises of the horses and wagons broke the quiet. There were five children in the group, of varied ages and sizes. They only whispered among themselves and stayed close to their mothers.

The four men from the last wagons grouped together, then approached the first wagon. One man stepped forward to help the woman down from her seat. He seemed to be holding a rag doll in his arms as he steadied her. Her long cotton dress had caught in the wagon wheel, and he loosened it for her.

The other women came forward slowly. Two of the women

stood on either side of the silent woman holding her up and speaking to her in soothing voices while the men pulled a small wooden box from the wagon.

Angie watched them without moving, but she had the feeling she could walk among them and they wouldn't know she was there. She hadn't noticed the open grave to her far left until now. The leaves had been cleared from the huge almost-bare maple tree and a mound of clay marked the spot. There was a small wooden cross already in place, but she couldn't see what was written on it from where she sat.

The men were carrying the box to the graveside. The man in the brown suit didn't seem to notice the tears that streamed down his face, making dark marks on the rough material of his suit.

A shiny object fell from his pocket as he passed her, shining brightly in the dead leaves. Angie sat still a moment. Then she moved slowly to pick it up. She started to reach out to him, but she drew back, slipping the object into her sweater pocket as she sat down again.

The women followed, their long skirts whispering with the leaves on the path, their shawls covering their heads. Two of them almost carrying the silent woman between them. The woman was so small, so frail looking. The group surrounded the grave as the men lowered the rough wooden box down on four ropes. One man reached into his jacket pocket and brought out a black book. He leafed through it, then started to read from it. His husky, low voice came out of the silence. "The Lord giveth and the Lord taketh away…"

"No! No!" The woman's shrill scream pierced the bright autumn day. The man with the prayer book stopped reading to look at her with pity in his eyes. The women clustered around her.

"Mary."

"Oh, Mary."

"Hush, Dear."

"We shouldn't have let her come," the oldest looking woman muttered under her breath.

The woman they called "Mary" quieted again and the man continued with the prayers. Now and then the group answered with a subdued "Amen" in one voice. When the prayers were finished, the women backed away as the men took shovels and started covering the box in its resting place.

The man in the dark brown suit moved slowly toward the tiny

woman. "Mary...Mary," he said, his voice so full of anguish that the sound tore at Angie's heart.

"Ed," the tiny woman raised her face for the first time. It was a small, lovely face, surrounded with brown curls, her large brown eyes filled with tears. "We can't leave her here! All alone! We can't!" She fell into his arms, and he rocked her there. Angie couldn't hear what he said as he tried to comfort her.

The other women had returned to their wagons, their bonnets bobbing as they spoke in whispers. The men finished filling the grave. Shovels carried over their shoulders, they too started towards their wagons.

The couple called "Ed" and "Mary" clung to each other as they gave one last look at the new grave, then they walked to their own wagon. Each wagon followed the next, turned in the clearing, and slowly disappeared down the winding, dirt road.

Angie shook herself. She felt exhausted, her heart heavy in her chest. She had never witnessed such sorrow in her life. She stood slowly, stretching her arms and moving her shoulders in a circular motion to bring her body awake.

She walked to the new grave and looked at the little wooden cross. It must have been made by hand. The words were formed by the placement of nail heads. It read:

KATHY
Born January 8, 1880
Died October 10, 1887
BELOVED DAUGHTER OF
ED & MARY BORDEAU

Angie felt weak. She read the dates once more. Then she turned and ran. She tripped, regained her balance, and ran again. She was just turning the last bend in the road when she saw her blue, late model, compact car, parked where she'd left it. She gasped aloud, "Thank God!"

She opened the car door and sat down in relief. She checked the calendar clipped to the visor. "October 1987, that's what it says," she said aloud. She thought, "I was in such a mood when I came here today. It must have been a morbid dream." She looked at the calendar again. Today was October 10th.

"I don't believe it," she muttered to herself as she swung her legs into the car to sit behind the wheel. She felt something heavy in her sweater pocket and reached to pull it out. It was a pocketknife. She turned it slowly in her hands. She gasped when she saw the initials "E.B." scratched neatly in the handle.

Memories - Not my Own
Rilla Anne DeBot Opelt

Sitting in silence
wondering on the mysteries of life -
resting in an ancient rocker
where so many have pondered before
holding in my hand a memory not my own
thoughts rolling back
to a time before I was

Imagining a little girl -
running barefoot down the dirt road
shoes in one hand to save them wear
tin syrup pail in the other filled with lunch
shouting laughing with others
on their way to school
dark eyes dancing beneath
this bright yellow knit hat
tassel bouncing
as she heads for her place
in the middle of the classroom
by the warm wood stove

Mother
smiling holding it close
you told me this was your favorite hat!
So when you had to leave your home
I promised I'd take it to mine

Sitting in silence
wondering on the mysteries of life -
watching you move restlessly
gasping for air
in this place you are

Looking at your pure white hair
your aged face
trying to find the child there
trying to find the young woman
who healed all my hurts

You look so different -
Yet I know that child
that woman
is still there

Treasuring memories you shared
keeping them safe
for my own little girls to ponder on
when I must follow where you go now.

I Never Heard My Father Sing
Mary L. Swanson

I never heard my father sing
And never wondered why,
Until I neared the age he was
When the dear man died.

I never heard my father sing
But often now in me
Murmurs of his memory
Hum a melody.

I never heard my father sing
So how did he impart
Music in the memories
Playing in my heart?

Masked Vigil
Elliott Crompton

Breathing
Nancy Larson

You sent us without ammunition
Human shields, to save, to sicken,
What did you think would happen?
Gasping premonition
Listening for truth
Ventilators—
You knew we
Would run
Out.

OK
Felicia Schneiderhan

You're ok
I tell myself, standing in the kitchen peeling long, thick carrots
The sudden wave of fear crashing at me.

You're ok
My mantra when I hear the neighborhood kids playing together
Touching hands to faces
Huddling close
My own kids, forbidden.

You're ok
My to-do list

You're ok, ok, ok.

The 4 p.m. grief. 2 a.m. anxiety. 7 a.m. fear.
It can be timed.
The placebo: You're ok.

(It's ok. Look around. Everything in place. Kids healthy. Money for
bills. Food in the fridge. Daily life, all together. We're ok. It's ok.
You're ok.)

Except it's a lie.

And then the other, quieter voice:
It's ok to say you're not _____ok.

The lie perpetuates the lie.
Management compels more failed management.
Anxiety suppresses the flame.

I am not *ok*.

Unspoken
  after Louise Erdrich's The Round House, 2012
Jill Lindl

If I could speak of it...
I would warn you that there are spirits here
They see what you are doing
If I could speak of it...
I would remind you of the sacredness of this place
It gives me the strength to endure your evil
If I could speak of it...
I would tell you I have no time for this shit
I'm late for dinner

If I could speak of it...
I would whisper it doesn't matter who did this awful thing
There will be no justice for me
If I could speak of it...
I would revel in your determination
But I am considered "something else" in eyes of the white law
If I could speak of it...
I would assure you that the wiindigo lives among us
Our ancestors are in council at this moment

If I could speak of it...
I would assuage the pain of my sweet boy
Why would I think life would be different for us
If I could speak of it...
I would reveal that the ancestors have chosen you
Our old law has obligations
If I could speak of it...
I would advise you to listen carefully to Grandfather's dreams
Therein lies elder wisdom

If I could speak of it...
I would call you nimise, my sister, niijikwe, my friend
Our bond defies comprehension
If I could speak of it...
I would assure you the wiindigo will regret your bestowed mercy
Wishing instead for an honorable death
If I could speak of it...

I would thank you for adopting the teachings
Of those who adopted you

If I could speak of it…
I would confess I knew of the plan the old buffalo woman had for
you
She speaks to me too
If I could speak of it…
I would disclose the identity of your spirit helpers
They were all around you
If I could speak of it…
I would mention my heart knew the moment it happened
It let out a sigh

If I could speak of it…
I would not. It doesn't matter
The wiindigo is gone
The ancestors have spoken
The old law has been upheld
The people go on
Blood memory will tell the story

Silence
Reflections on reading David Treuer's "The Clouds Overhead," 2006
Joy Armstrong

Did you ever notice even in complete silence there is a slender
ribbon of sound?
as if someone/something is whispering for your attention.
Treuer writes of an Indian silence.
I write of a different silence.
A white silence.
It's the silence of not knowing there is a Native American population.
It's the silence of living on land that is not yours.
It's the silence of most white people.

If you live in a town near a reservation,
look around when you're out and about.
Look for English and Anisinaabemowin.
Look in stores
in hospitals, in medical clinics,
in libraries,
where you eat out.
See any words you don't recognize because they are Ojibwe
words?
No?
Why change?
No one is complaining.
It doesn't matter.

But it does matter!
It matters
For equality,
For justice,

Remember.

Remember
the silence,
the slender ribbon of sound,
someone/something is whispering for your attention.
Listen!
Please.
Miigwech (Thanks)

Your Voice Now Protects
Nina Woerheide

Imprisoned by the chains of your mind
that hold you back like the hands
that once held you down,
your words still sometimes can't find their way
out of your mouth.
You wanted to scream out the universe
but your words
they couldn't find their way
out of your mouth.
You never thought it could happen to you.
You always thought
it will probably be her—
that slutty girl.
That girl that gets in an Uber while she's drunk.
The Uber driver will probably be the one that does it.
You never thought it would be you,
but it was.
And you walked away with scars.
Your voice rolls out of your heart and off your tongue
not like a cowardly puppy, but like a stampede of bison.
No more silence.
Your voice now protects.

"Soulmate" Is Cliché
Nina Woerheide

They say that before you ever catch a glimpse
of your perfectly fitting puzzle piece,
your trails will have intertwined like the paths of two snakes,
at least once.
And the two of you will have participated in a one-act play,
where each of you played the significantly-insignificant role of
passersby.
You were probably too busy looking
at the sheet section in Target to notice him walk by
though he could have observed you.

But I don't want to conduct one of those boundless romance
recitals,
where Mr. muscle-bronze skin
hoards more than his share of the novel
and spends every last paper fiber and every last inkblot
attempting to seduce his feminine counterpart.

Heartbeat of the Earth
Marlene Wisuri

Being Seen by Bagwajinini
Carter Meland

For the last ten years I have been trying to make sense out of why I like to think about Bigfoot.

For the last thirty years I have been trying to make sense out of what it means to be an unenrolled descendant of Anishinaabe people, to be someone who didn't even know about this legacy until he was nearly thirty years old. I was a lost descendant.

A few years ago it occurred to me that these two things are related as I began to explore stories about Bagwajinini and Sabe, the names by which Bigfoot is known in Anishinaabemowin. One story I found has subsequently become one that stands at the center of my attempts to make sense out of both Bagwajinini and my Anishinaabe descendancy. An internet search for stories about Bigfoot in Minnesota led me to an article in the *Duluth News Tribune* by Lee Bloomquist, dated October 13, 2007. Profiling prominent Bigfoot researchers in northern Minnesota, the article also contains the stories the researchers tell about the forest people. The one that caught my eye was told by Donald Sherman, a member of the Leech Lake band of Ojibwe. The story he tells about a woman driving near Bena is only three sentences long. She sees Bagwajinini and he looks at her. She begins to cry because, as Sherman states, the forest being "looked into her soul."

That's as much of the story as we get, but I wanted more. I like to think my way into these Bigfoot stories. It's my way of finding out what these stories might mean in my search to figure out why I like Bigfoot stories. That soul thing and that breaking down crying thing are powerful, so I imagined this story. It's not about that woman that Sherman talks about; she has her own story and, as far as I know, she has never publicly said anything beyond those parts Sherman shares with us. This story that I'm thinking about concerns another woman who, like the first, is driving to Bena, and like the first one we don't know why and not even my story is willing to guess. Actually, my story has numerous guesses, but no certainties that any of those guesses are anywhere near the truth. Sometimes even our imaginary creations have a right to their privacy. Let's see where her story takes us:

The trees of the northwoods, white pine and red pine, bend at the edge of her vision as the car speeds down the road. From that peripheral perspective they seem to dip toward the ground as she passes by, but then they rise up again from the earth if she glances into the rearview mirror. She aims to make Bena before too long. Capital of the Leech Lake Anishinaabe nation in what is currently known as northern Minnesota. Bena is her home. Perhaps.

The trees press up against the road, keep her car focused forward, moving toward something in Bena, but the story doesn't make it clear why she's heading there. Maybe she's heading to an ailing grandparent or toward ceremony; perhaps she's been away from her community for a year or a decade or a lifetime and is seeking to renew connections she'd neglected for too long, even if she's maybe only really been gone three months. She's moving toward something in Bena is all we know for sure.

Deep in the woods around her, back where the soil thins, jack pines grow from some of the most unforgiving ground. Pawprints, hoofprints, and footprints cross and recross one another on the paths back there amid the pine, evidence of the lives in the forest encoded in the twisting helixes of trackways in the dirt. These traces conjure familiar deer and chipmunks, but also the rarer moose and wolf, and rarest of all, perhaps, Bagwajinini. The forest person, elder sibling to the Anishinaabe. Their footprints are as long as a tall man's forearm, longer even. Their stride covers five or six feet at a step. The thin soil holds all these tracks, including Bagwajinini's, memories of moments from passing lives. These moments swirl away in a stiff breeze or are pounded deep into the ground when the thunders come.

Ahead is a break in the trees, that sort of break that barely even registers consciously when we've been on the road for a while, but which still draws the eye. A railroad line crosses the two lanes of the state highway. No bells are ringing, no lights flashing, so she approaches at speed and, again in that unthinking way we get when on the road, she glances down the tracks and sees him there, standing at the top of the railroad embankment, rising from the stones along the tracks. Really, he towers there, taller than any person she's ever seen, dark hair covering his body. He looks straight into her eyes, his head turning to follow her as she speeds past, and she begins to cry. She feels the weight of his gaze as the railroad tracks recede and the trees rise again in the rearview mirror.

We don't know whether her tears came in great heaving sobs or as a gentle release of pent-up emotion. This story doesn't go that far, but she will later tell people that she cried because Bagwajinini had looked into her soul. Hers.

He took it in as she sped by, saw something valuable nested there, I think, and so the tears came. He understood something about her and in that brief glimpse of him, she suddenly understood something about herself that she'd long wondered. As lost as she might have felt throughout her life, or over the last decade, or in the past year, even if she's maybe only really felt that way for three months, she suddenly understood she was going to be fine. He had seen her soul. He had seen her.

Like I said I like to think my way into these Bigfoot stories as a means of trying to figure out why I attach so much importance to them. Like I said, too, our family's Anishinaabe descendance had been lost to us for decades; family members have lived and died and never known it. That woman I imagine in the story, who has a whole life and dreams and regrets that I can never know, must have felt lost to have such an emotional response to Bigfoot seeing her. Her tears stem from neither sorrow, nor joy, nor happiness. They stem from relief, from being found when all might have otherwise seemed lost.

In that news article, Donald Sherman explains to the reporter that Creator sent the Bigfoot people to the Anishinaabeg for many reasons, including as a way of warning people of impending illness. Illness may not be just a physical ailment, I'm supposing, but could also speak to a loss of spiritual balance, that harmony you seek to maintain within as well as with the greater human and more-than-human community, including your ancestors, that is key to living mino-bimaadiziwin. Mino-bimaadiziwin, the Anishinaabe "good life," is that way of living with harmony and balance that reflects both spiritual and physical well-being.

Sherman also told the reporter that Creator sent the Bigfoot beings to guide and care for the Anishinaabeg. "Bigfoot teaches us medicine through our medicine man," Sherman said.

I am trying to understand this Bigfoot trait of guiding and caring, of teaching medicine, as pointing to the sort of abiding compassion that some might call a blessing. It is the sort of compassion that comes without conditions and is weighted with the sort of keen concern someone has for those who may need help. From other teachers I have learned that Bagwajinini also comes to people who have lost their way in the woods, particularly those who are seeking medicine. If such a person has good thoughts, Bagwajinini will help them find the medicine they seek and, if they are lost, will set them on the path home.

He came to that woman along the railroad embankment and he comes to me in the stories told about him. Important stories need to be understood as medicine in that Native sense of the word, as something given in compassion and filled with healing potential. I think about the decades and lifetimes of our family's separation from our Anishinaabe identity, how it was lost to us, and I think about how Bagwajinini started coming to me in cheap paperback books and cheesy TV documentaries when I was probably no more than nine or ten years old, started looking for me twenty years before we even knew we were Anishinaabe descendants, and found me at long last when he looked into that woman's soul and blessed me with her story.

Contributor's Notes

Lisa Poje Angelos is a park ranger by day, poet by night. Originally from Milwaukee, Wisconsin, she now lives and works in Carlton, Minnesota. Her writing has appeared in various publications and collaborative exhibitions. She is happiest when in the woods and in the company of dear ones and animals.

Joy Armstrong is currently a student at Fond du Lac Tribal and Community College. Joy retired from ministry in 2004. She loves to read, write and study. She returned to classes three years ago. She enjoys acquiring new knowledge and meeting new people. At eighty, Joy is calm, intelligent and a good listener. She will graduate in May 2021. She is looking forward to new adventures.

Govinda Budrow is a mother to four children, two born to her and two born of her heart. She is an Ojibwe educator that worked for 16 years in as a classroom teacher. She now is an education faculty member at Fond du Lac Tribal and Community College (FDLTCC).

Dakota Burton is a former FDLTCC student, and a current student at Bethel University in St Paul, Minnesota. She is a Social Studies Education major, and a Junior. In her free time, she enjoys writing, reading, watching movies and tv, exploring the North Shore, and spending time with her family.

Jan Chronister (Maple, Wisconsin) retired from teaching at FDLTCC in 2015. She has published four chapbooks and two full-length poetry collections. Jan currently serves as president of the Wisconsin Fellowship of Poets.
www.janchronisterpoetry.wordpress.com

Elliott Crompton grew up in Madison, Wisconsin, and lived in both Missouri and Virginia before making Two Harbors, Minnesota his home. He studied history and design at Virginia Tech and continues to learn through woodworking, block printing, and writing.

Clair Friedman is a 21-year-old student who is finishing her Associate's Degree this summer semester. She plans to continue her education to become a school counselor. She works as an Assistant Teacher at Wood City Preschool. She likes to spend most of her free-time with her fiancé, Joe, her son, Dylan, and her brother, Rolo.

In her essay "My Black Garbage Bag Life: Life in the System," **Tricia Gottschalk** talks about how she went through being mistreated in her first two foster homes to being cared for in her final home. Tricia is now a strong and smart woman who is thankful for the Reynolds family that took her in when she had no place else to go and no one to love her.

Francis Hadley is a senior at UW Superior in its writing program. He enjoys writing about the beauty of the Northwoods and his various travels. He lives with his fiancé and Jack Russell terrier in Chippewa Falls, WI. He spends his free time writing fantastic adventures for Dungeons and Dragons.

Denise Huckabee is a 40-year-old single mother of 3 who has recently returned to college for an LADC. She was born and raised in Georgia and moved to Minnesota in 2019 for a change of scenery and a new start. She loves Fond du Lac, is excited about her future career, and hopes to start an internship in 2021.

Meridel Kahl retired in 2013 after 45 years of teaching. She spent the last 27 years of her career at The College of St. Scholastica in Duluth, Minnesota. Her poems have appeared in *WritersRead, The Talking Stick, The Peninsula Pulse, Amethyst and Agate: Poems of Lake Superior, The Thunderbird Review, The Avocet, Bramble,* and *Leaves of Peace.*

Maggie Kazel is a former San Franciscan, North Carolinian, Eastern seaboarder, and when her daughter turned five moved to be closer to Lake Superior. Published in many journals, but lacking nine lives, Maggie lives by the words of Grace Paley "Life is too short, and Art too long!"

Laura Krueger-Kochmann is a college English instructor who loves to write poetry and fiction. She finds inspiration in memories, canoe trips, and bedtime stories. Laura has spent most of her life in Wisconsin and Minnesota and enjoys living in Duluth with her husband, Todd, and her daughter, Cordelia.

Nancy Larson lives in Ashland County, Wisconsin. In her career with the Wisconsin Department of Natural Resources, she worked on the cleanup of the St. Louis River Estuary, and she stays very connected to the Twin Ports.

Bradley Limanen is an aspiring author from the Twin Cities area. After attending Fond Du Lac Tribal and Community College for a post-secondary education, he now seeks to write stories inspired by elements of his life, and his home state of Minnesota.

Jill Lindl is Ojibwe, descendent of White Earth Reservation. Jill works full time as an academic and cultural advisor to American Indian middle and high school students in a large Twin Cities suburban school district. She is also a Sociology student and is studying Anishinaabe language.

Mason Martin is a sociology instructor at FDLTCC. He is married to Danielle Fagen with 4 beautiful children. He currently is exploring many different hobbies and passions from painting to making wooden spoons. One of the things he truly enjoys is making masks for friends, family, and others. Although not the best tailor, he hopes it helps.

Carter Meland (Anishinaabe descendant) is a writer, bicycle rider, bigfoot meditator, and Professor of American Indian Studies at the University of Minnesota, Duluth. His novel *Stories for a Lost Child* was a finalist for the 2018 Minnesota Book Awards and he is currently working on a creative nonfiction book, *Strange Spirits: A Memoir in Monsters*, both of which explore the power of Anishinaabe storytelling as a way to make sense of fractured family identities and our fractured relationship to our living environments.

Liz Minette's garden this year produced a lot of spaghetti squash that she has not written a poem about, yet. This past year her non-spaghetti squash poems have found homes in Blue Collar Review and The Thunderbird Review. Currently, she is writing poem recipes for spaghetti squash.

Rilla Anne DeBot Opelt was born and raised in Duluth, Minnesota and has been writing since 6th grade—short stories, articles, and poetry. Her work has been published in *The Thunderbird Review,*

Spring Thaw, others locally. Rilla Anne is a member of Lake Superior Writers, Wisconsin Writers, and former Duluth Manuscript Club. She is currently working on her memoirs and chapbooks for publication.

A graduate of the University of Arizona (BA Speech/English) and the University of Minnesota, Duluth (MEd), **Gregory Opstad** is a retired teacher. He divides his time between homes in Cloquet, Minnesota and Cochiti Lake, New Mexico. A member of Lake Superior Writers, his poems have appeared in the *North Coast Review; The Rag; Migrations: Poetry & Prose for Life's Transitions; Trail Guide to the Northland Experience; Liberty's Vigil: The Occupy Anthology, 99 Poets for the 99%, More Voices of New Mexico*, and *Manzano Mountain Review*. His chapbook, *Lake Country*, was released by Finishing Line Press in 2013.

Diana Randolph, Drummond, writes and paints in her home studio nestled in Chequamegon/Nicolet National Forest. She loves silent sports throughout the different seasons and gardening. She teaches art workshops for adults. She's the author of *Beacons of the Earth and Sky* that contains her art and poetry. Please visit www.dianarandolph.com.

Deborah Rasmussen retired from her nursing career in Florida to Duluth in 2012. Her poems have appeared on the Lake Superior Writers website, on RattlePoetry.com, in *Thunderbird Review, Talking Stick, Barstow & Grand,* and *The Writer.* Her stories for children have appeared in *Cricket, Pockets*, and *Highlights for Children* magazines.

Kit Rohrbach has been searching for documented connections between the similar patterns of Ojibwe beadwork and Jacobean crewel embroidery. She hasn't found them yet but remains fascinated by both art forms.

Babette Sandman graduated from University of Minnesota Duluth in 1988 from the American Indian Mental Health Training Project. She and her husband Skip Sandman have been married for 30 years living in Duluth. Babette is active in the community. Together they have 3 daughters, 9 grandchildren, 1 great grandchild.

Felicia Schneiderhan's short stories and personal essays have appeared in many national journals, magazines, and anthologies. She lives in Duluth with her husband and their three tsunamis. Read more of her award-winning articles, personal essays, and fiction, plus her adventure blog, at www.feliciaschneiderhan.com.

Sara Sha is a lifelong Minnesota resident and a recent Duluth transplant. Besides writing, she enjoys historical research and wandering through the woods and rocky areas of Northeastern Minnesota with her husband. She can also be found on the shores of Lake Superior talking to stones.

Jim Springett started his love of art at the Toledo Museum of Art in 1952 when he was 5 years old. He did not start to paint until 1991 and continues today. Today he paints the birds of Crex Meadows Wildlife Area. He is also a masterful watercolorist.

Tekla Stolberg, a former FDLTCC student, believes that writing is one of the best ways to share your soul with another. Through use of words, you can paint a picture that shares your heart and experiences. It is her hope that her poems reach those that will resonate with them the most.

Mary L. Swanson lives in the woods near Willow River, Minnesota, with her best friend / husband. She enjoys adventures with her daughters and writing little ditties for her grandchildren. Nature gives her inspiration and peace.

Matthew Tillman resides in Orlando Fl. He loves to play football and wants to one day to pursue playing football for the NFL. He is a fun, loving, kind person that enjoys spending time outdoors. His daily motto is "Before greatness is achieved your comfort zone needs to be disturbed."

Peggy Trojan divides her time between Brule and Eau Claire, Wisconsin. She has published four chapbooks and two full-length poetry collections.

Lucy Tyrrell lives near Bayfield, Wisconsin. Her poetry is inspired by nature and wild landscapes, outdoor pursuits (mushing, hiking, canoeing), travel, and her everyday experiences. Lucy Tyrrell lives by her favorite verbs—*experience* and *create*.

Jamie Williams is a current student at FDLTCC.

Marlene Wisuri has been a college teacher, artist/photographer, and author. Her art has appeared in exhibitions throughout the United States and internationally. She is the co-author of books dealing with immigration, local history, and Ojibwe culture. She is the chair of the Sami Cultural Center of North America. Her home on the North Shore of Lake Superior provides inspiration for her life and work.

Nina Woerheide is a young poet and creative writer. Focusing primarily on short story and novel, a lifetime of writing has directed her to the focal point of poetic expression. All of her work is based on real-life experiences.

Marie Zhuikov is a novelist, science writer, and poet from Duluth, Minnesota. Her most recent work is "Going Coastal: An Anthology of Lake Superior Short Stories" (2017 North Star Press), which she edited and co-authored. It won honorable mention from the Northeastern Minnesota Book Awards. For more information, visit marieZwrites.com.

Made in the USA
Monee, IL
20 April 2021